Instructor's Guide to Accompany STRUCTURED FORTRAN 77 for Engineers and Scientists

second edition

Instructor's Guide to Accompany
STRUCTURED FORTRAN 77 FOR ENGINEERS AND SCIENTISTS

second edition

D. M. ETTER
University of New Mexico, Albuquerque

Prepared with assistance from Vena Margo, Leslie Brown, and Jae Kerr

The Benjamin/Cummings Publishing Company, Inc.
Menlo Park, California • Reading, Massachusetts •
Don Mills, Ontario • Wokingham, U.K. • Amsterdam •
Sydney • Singapore • Tokyo • Madrid • Bogota •
Santiago • San Juan

ISBN 0-8053-2496-8

ABCDEFGHIJ-AL-8987

The Benjamin/Cummings Publishing Company, Inc.
2727 Sand Hill Rd.
Menlo Park, CA 94025

PREFACE

A number of items have been included in this Instructor's Guide to supplement the material presented in the Second Edition of STRUCTURED FORTRAN 77 FOR ENGINEERS AND SCIENTISTS.

COURSE SYLLABUS

Two forms of a course syllabus are given, one for a semester course and one for a quarter course. In addition to containing specific topics, corresponding reading assignments are also included.

SOFTWARE SUPPLEMENT

A software supplement is available that allows students to interact with the problems and programs presented in the 26 special Application sections within the text. This drill package is user interactive and menu driven. Students can ask the package to copy a program solution into a file which can then be compiled and executed. The drill package will also suggest changes for the student to make in the program. After the student makes and tests the suggested modification, the drill package will provide a completed solution for the student to compare to his or her solution.

QUIZ BANK DESCRIPTION

A QUIZ BANK is also available and contains 150 quizzes which are printed one per page to allow simple copying of the pages for use in classroom quizzes. Midterm and final exams are also included for class distribution as actual exams or as practice exams. Solutions for the quizzes and exams are included in the QUIZ BANK. The quiz bank information is also available on a diskette.

VIEWGRAPHS

Fifty viewgraphs have been prepared using large print so that they can be copied directly onto transparencies. These viewgraphs represent selected material that covers the entire text.

ADDITIONAL COMPUTER PROJECTS AND SOLUTIONS

Additional computer projects, sample data files, sample output, and sample solutions are included to supplement those at the end of the chapters in the text. This information is also available on a diskette.

SOLUTIONS TO TEXT PROBLEMS

Many of the solutions to text problems are included at the end of the text. The remaining solutions are included here so that a complete set of solutions is available. The solutions are also available on a diskette.

TABLE OF CONTENTS

CHAPTER 1 - COURSE SYLLABUS

Semester Syllabus

WEEK	TOPIC	READING ASSIGNMENT
1	Introduction to course and to computers	Chapter 1
2	Simple programs with arithmetic computations	Chapter 2
3	IF structures and WHILE loops	Chapter 3, Sections 1-4
4	DO loops	Chapter 3, Sections 5-8
5	Data files	Chapter 4, Sections 1-3
6	One-dimensional arrays	Chapter 5, Section 1-4
7	Two-dimensional arrays	Chapter 5, Section 5-7
8	Review and midterm exam	
9	Function subprograms	Chapter 6
10	Subroutine subprograms	Chapter 7
11	Character data, Double-precision data, Complex data	Chapter 8
12	Additional file handling	Chapter 9
13	Numerical applications	Chapter 10, Sections 1-5
14	Numerical applications	Chapter 10, Sections 6-7
15	Review and final exam	

Quarter Syllabus

WEEK	TOPIC	READING ASSIGNMENT
1	Introduction to course and to computers	Chapter 1
2	Simple programs with arithmetic computations	Chapter 2
3	IF structures and WHILE loops	Chapter 3, Sections 1-4
4	DO loops, Data files	Chapter 3, Sections 5-8 Chapter 4, Sections 1-3
5	One-dimensional arrays	Chapter 5, Section 1-4
6	Review and midterm exam	
7	Two-dimensional arrays	Chapter 5, Section 5-7
8	Function subprograms	Chapter 6
9	Subroutine subprograms	Chapter 7
10	Review and final exam	

CHAPTER 2 - SOFTWARE SUPPLEMENT

Since learning is an active rather than a passive process, we have designed a software supplement to work in conjunction with the text. This supplement consists of a set of interactive files that contain solutions to the 26 special Application sections contained in the text so that students can immediately begin running and playing with these programs. Once a student understands a program, the software supplement will suggest simple changes that will either improve the program or give it an additional operation to perform. Because the original program file already exists, changes require only minor editing steps before the student is ready to test the modifications. This procedure emphasizes hands-on experience with the programs as they are being studied.

This drill package is user interactive and menu driven. It is comprised of several sections which interact with the user in different ways. The user is required to enter his or her name and social security number each time the drill package is used. A new user of the package is shown an introductory screen. This screen welcomes new users and acquaints them with the capabilities of the package. Next, a menu system aids the user in choosing a particular area (such as one-dimensional arrays) to study. From the secondary menu, the user chooses a particular Application program. The user is given the problem description which explains the the problem to be solved, and then copies the solution into a file chosen by the user. The drill package ends automatically to give the user a chance to compile and run the new program. When the drill package is invoked again, it will remember exactly where the user is within the package. The user is asked if he or she would like to try a modification to the program. After attempting the modifications, the drill package will provide a correct solution and output so that the student can check the modifications. Users are able to view their history within the drill package at any time in order to check their progress through the package.

The Software Supplement (or drill package) is available to instructors using STRUCTURED FORTRAN 77 FOR ENGINEERS AND SCIENTISTS (Second Edition) in two forms. An object file stored on an IBM PC compatible diskette is available and is ready to run on IBM PC compatible computers. A source file and accompanying data files are also available so that the code (in FORTRAN 77) can be uploaded and compiled on other systems.

CHAPTER 3 - QUIZ BANK DESCRIPTION

A separate supplement, the QUIZ BANK, is also available to instructors using STRUCTURED FORTRAN 77 FOR ENGINEERS AND SCIENTISTS (Second Edition). Ten sets of quizzes, corresponding to the 10 chapters in the text, are included in this separate supplement. Each set of quizzes contains 10, 15, or 20 quizzes, depending on the complexity of each chapter. Each quiz is printed on a separate page to allow simple copying of the quiz for classroom use. The solutions to all the quizzes are included.

Two midterm exams and two final exams are also included, in a form that can easily be copied for class distribution as either actual exams or as practice exams. Solutions for these exams are again included.

A diskette containing all the quiz files and exam files is also available upon request to the publisher.

CHAPTER 4 - VIEWGRAPHS

Fifty viewgraphs have been prepared using large print so that they can be copied directly onto transparencies. These viewgraphs represent selected material that covers the entire text.

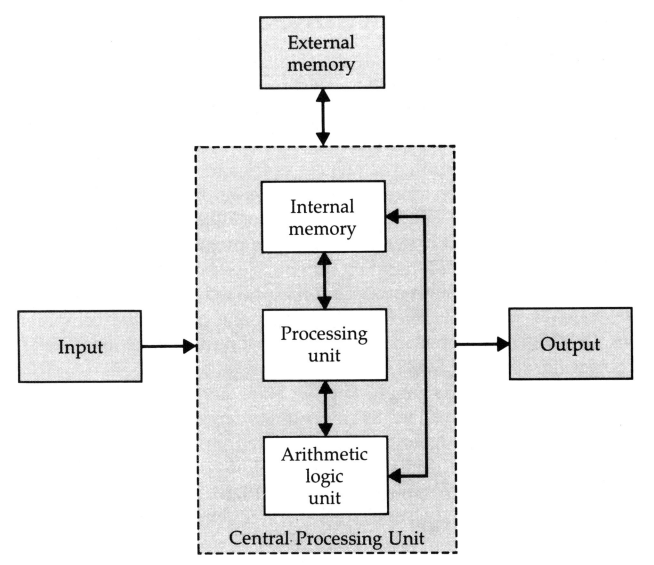

Block diagram of a computer.

Examples of High-Level Languages

LANGUAGE	EXAMPLE STATEMENTS
| FORTRAN 77 | ```
IF (HOURS.LE.40.0) THEN
     SALARY = HOURS*PAYRTE
ELSE
     SALARY = 40.0*PAYRTE +
              (HOURS - 40.0)*PAYRTE*1.5
ENDIF
``` |
| Pascal | ```
IF HOURS <= 40.0 THEN
     SALARY := HOURS*PAYRATE
ELSE
     SALARY := 40.0*PAYRATE +
               (HOURS - 40.0)*PAYRATE*1.5;
``` |
| Ada | ```
IF HOURS <= 40.0 THEN
     SALARY := HOURS*PAYRATE;
ELSE
     SALARY := 40.0*PAYRATE +
               (HOURS - 40.0)*PAYRATE*1.5;
``` |
| BASIC | ```
    IF H > 40.0 THEN 200
    LET S = H*P
    GO TO 250
200 LET S = 40.0*P + (H - 40.0)*P*1.5
250
``` |
| COBOL | ```
IF HOURS IS LESS THAN 40.0 OR
   HOURS IS EQUAL TO 40.0,
     COMPUTE SALARY = HOURS*PAYRATE
ELSE
     COMPUTE SALARY = 40.0*PAYRATE +
               (HOURS - 40.0)*PAYRATE*1.5.
``` |
| PL/I | ```
IF HOURS <= 40.0 THEN
     SALARY = HOURS*PAYRATE;
ELSE
     SALARY = 40.0*PAYRATE +
              (HOURS - 40.0)*PAYRATE*1.5;
``` |
| ALGOL | ```
IF HOURS ≤ 40.0 THEN
     SALARY := HOURS X PAYRATE
ELSE
     SALARY := 40.0 X PAYRATE +
               (HOURS - 40.0) X PAYRATE X 1.5;
``` |
```

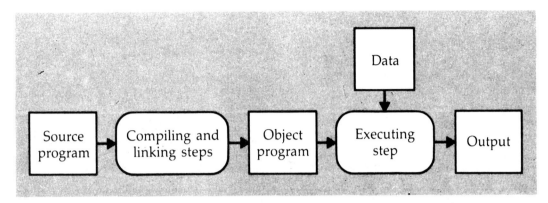

Compilation-linkage-execution process for running a computer program.

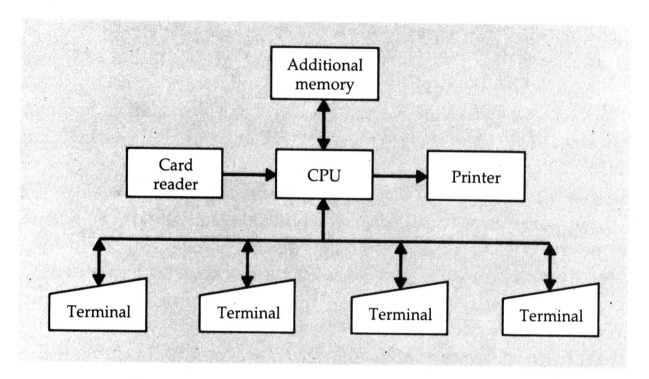

Computer system with batch processing and time sharing.

FORTRAN PROGRAM

```
*----------------------------------------------------------------*
      PROGRAM   COMPUT
*
* This program computes the average of
* a set of experimental data values.
*
      INTEGER   COUNT
      REAL  X, SUM, AVERG
*
      SUM = 0.0
      COUNT = 0
      READ*, X
    1 IF (X.NE.0.0) THEN
         SUM = SUM + X
         COUNT = COUNT + 1
         READ*, X
         GO TO 1
      ENDIF
      AVERG = SUM/REAL(COUNT)
      PRINT 5, AVERG
    5 FORMAT (1X,'THE AVERAGE IS ',F6.2)
      END
*------------------------------------------------------------
```

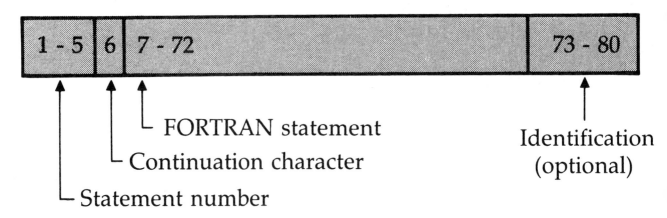

General form of a FORTRAN statement.

AMOUNT	36.84	VOLUME	183.0
RATE	0.065	TOTAL	486.5
TEMP	17.5	INFO	72

DISTANCE	Invalid name—too long
TIME	Valid name
PI	Valid name
$	Invalid name—illegal character ($)
TAX—RT	Invalid name—illegal character (—)
B1	Valid name
2X	Invalid name—first character must be alphabetic

DECIMAL VALUE	SCIENTIFIC NOTATION	EXPONENTIAL NOTATION
3,876,000,000	3.876×10^9	0.3876E10
0.0000010053	1.0053×10^{-6}	0.10053E−05
−8,030,000	-8.03×10^6	−0.803E07
−0.000157	-1.57×10^{-4}	−0.157E−03

Typical Ranges for FORTRAN Data Values

Computer	Real Value Ranges	Maximum Integer
IBM 360/370	Mantissa: 6 significant digits Exponent: -77 to 75	2,147,483,647
VAX	Mantissa: 7 significant digits Exponent: -38 to 38	2,147,483,647
CRAY-1	Mantissa: 13 significant digits Exponent: -2465 to 2465	2.8×10^{14}
CDC 6000/7000	Mantissa: 14 significant digits Exponent: -293 to 322	9.2×10^{18}

Arithmetic Operations in Algebraic Form and in FORTRAN

Operation	Algebraic Form	FORTRAN
Addition	$A + B$	A + B
Subtraction	$A - B$	A − B
Multiplication	$A \times B$	A*B
Division	$\dfrac{A}{B}$	A/B
Exponentiation	A^3	A**3

Priorities of Arithmetic Operations

PRIORITY	OPERATION
First	Parentheses
Second	Exponentiation
Third	Multiplication and division
Fourth	Addition and subtraction

Common Intrinsic Functions

FUNCTION NAME AND ARGUMENT	FUNCTION VALUE	COMMENT
SQRT(X)	$\sqrt{X}$	Square root of X
ABS(X)	$\lvert X \rvert$	Absolute value of X
SIN(X)	Sine of angle X	X must be in radians
COS(X)	Cosine of angle X	X must be in radians
TAN(X)	Tangent of angle X	X must be in radians
EXP(X)	e^x	e raised to the X power
LOG(X)	$\log_e X$	Natural log of X
LOG10(X)	$\log_{10} X$	Common log of X
INT(X)	Integer part of X	Converts a real value to an integer value
REAL(I)	Real value of I	Converts an integer value to a real value
MOD(I,J)	Integer remainder of I/J	Remainder or modulo function

Output buffer

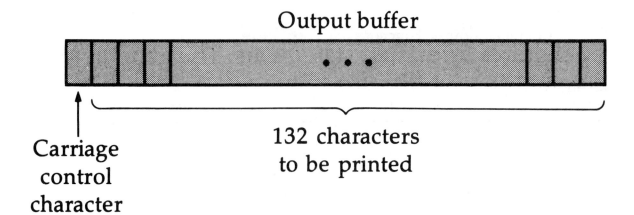

Carriage
control
character

132 characters
to be printed

CARRIAGE CONTROL CHARACTER	VERTICAL SPACING
1	New page
blank	Single spacing
0	Double spacing
+	No vertical spacing

In Chapter 1 we presented a five-step design process for problem solving:

1. State the problem clearly.
2. Describe the input and the output.
3. Work a sample problem by hand.
4. Develop an algorithm to solve the problem.
5. Test the algorithm carefully.

If GPA > 3.0 then
    Print ID
    honor roll ← honor roll + 1

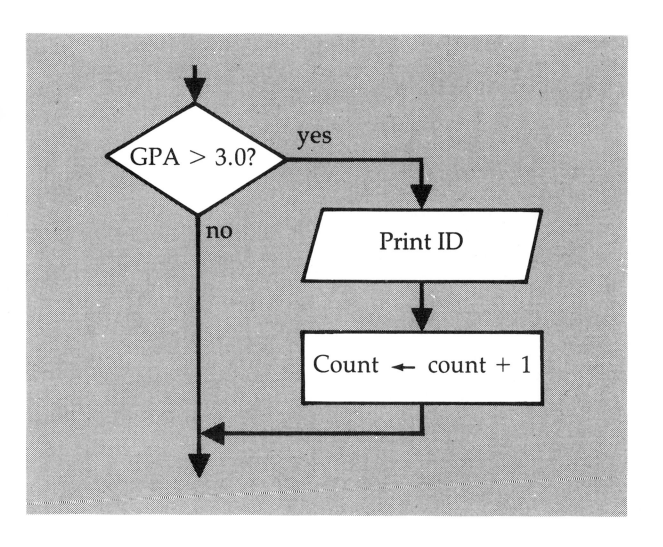

If GPA > 3.0 then
   Print ID, GPA
   honor roll ← honor roll + 1
Else
   Print ID

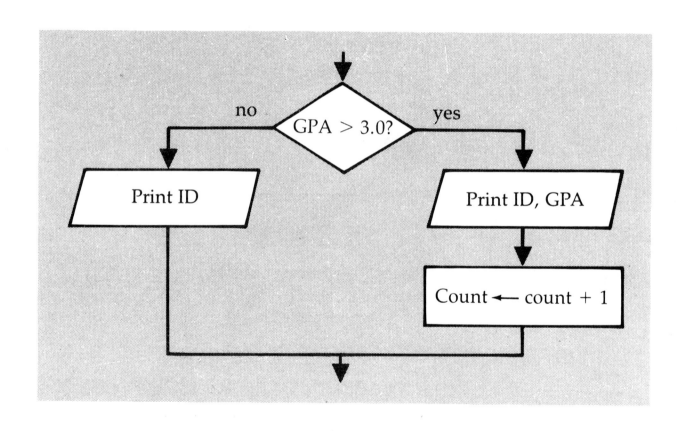

```
If GPA > 3.5 then
    Print ID, GPA, '*'
    president's count ← president's count + 1
Else If GPA > 3.0 then
    Print ID, GPA
    dean's count ← dean's count + 1
Else
    Print ID
```

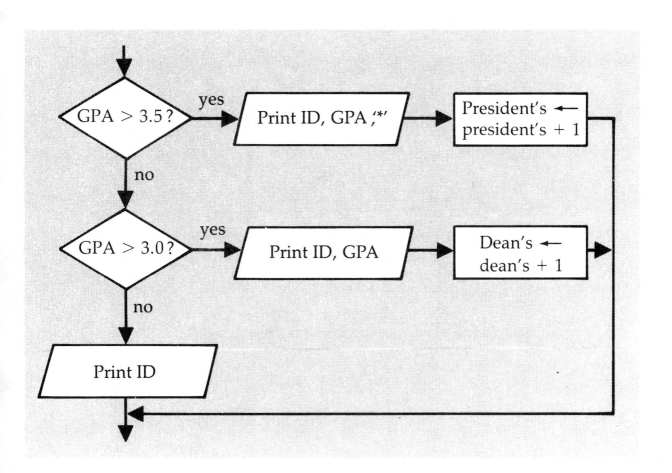

While sum < 1000 do
   Read data value
   sum ← sum + data value
Print sum

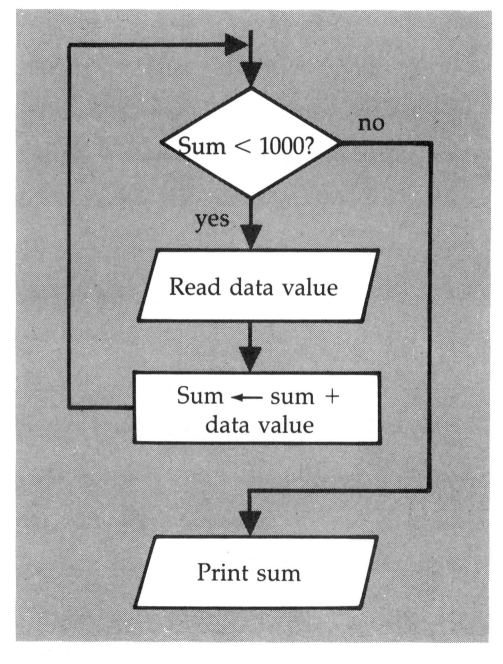

count ← 0
While count < 10 do
    (processing of data)
    count ← count + 1

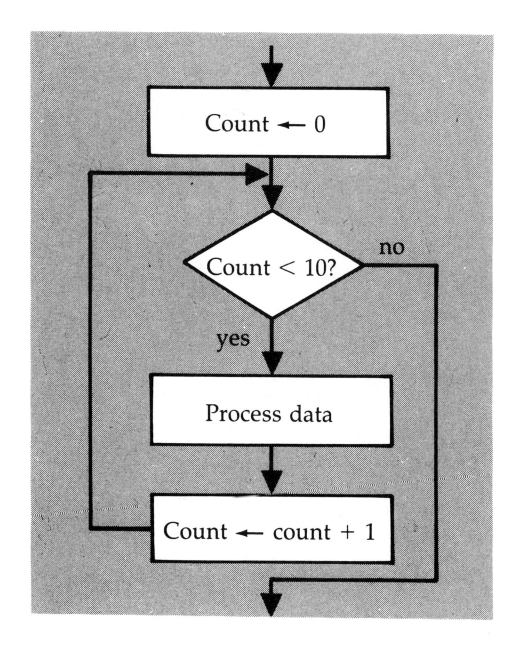

RELATIONAL OPERATOR	INTERPRETATION
.EQ.	Is equal to
.NE.	Is not equal to
.LT.	Is less than
.LE.	Is less than or equal to
.GT.	Is greater than
.GE.	Is greater than or equal to

```
IF  (condition)    THEN
       statement 1
       .
       .
       .
       statement n
ENDIF
```

```
IF (condition) THEN
    statement 1
        .
        .
        .
    statement n
ELSE
    statement n + 1
        .
        .
        .
    statement m
ENDIF
```

```
IF (condition 1) THEN
    statement 1
    .
    .
    .
    statement m
ELSEIF (condition 2) THEN
    statement m + 1
    .
    .
    .
    statement n
ELSEIF (condition 3) THEN
    statement n + 1
    .
    .
    .
    statement p
ELSE
    statement p + 1
    .
    .
    .
    statement q
ENDIF
```

While condition do
statement 1
.

.

.

.

statement m
statement p

```
n  IF (condition) THEN
      statement 1
         .
         .
         .
      statement m
      GO TO n
   ENDIF
```

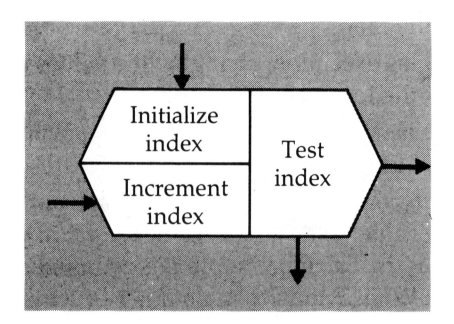

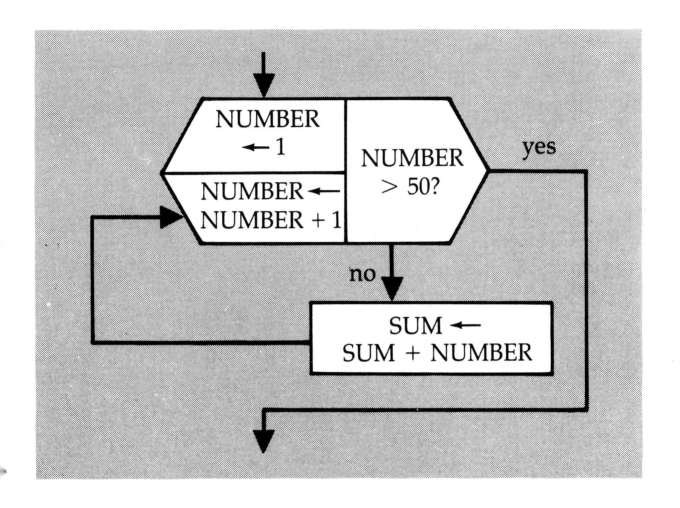

```
*-----------------------------------------------------------------*
      PROGRAM  NEST
*
*  This program prints the indexes in nested DO loops.
*
      INTEGER  I, J
*
      PRINT*, '  I   J'
      PRINT*
      DO 20 I=1,5
          DO 10 J=3,1,-1
              PRINT 5, I, J
   5          FORMAT (1X,I3,1X,I3)
  10      CONTINUE
          PRINT*, 'END OF PASS'
  20 CONTINUE
      END
*-----------------------------------------------------------------*
```

J(1)	2
J(2)	−5
J(3)	14
J(4)	80
J(5)	−12

1.2	−0.8	36.9	−0.07

DIST(1) DIST(2) DIST(3) DIST(4)

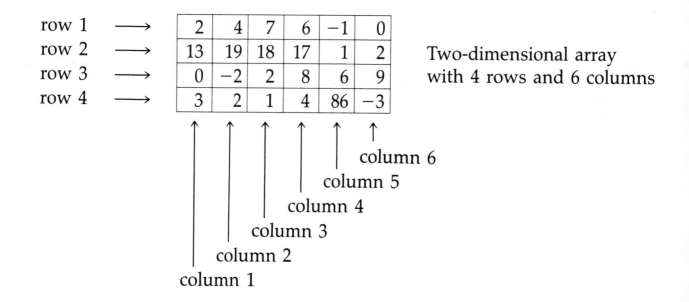

row 1 ⟶
row 2 ⟶
row 3 ⟶
row 4 ⟶

2	4	7	6	−1	0
13	19	18	17	1	2
0	−2	2	8	6	9
3	2	1	4	86	−3

Two-dimensional array
with 4 rows and 6 columns

column 6
column 5
column 4
column 3
column 2
column 1

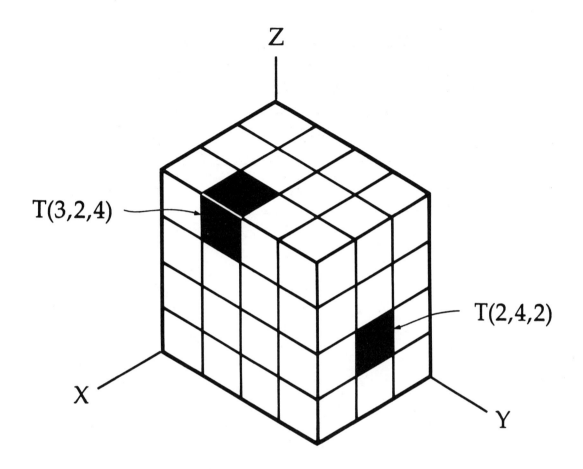

Common Memory Area

A	57.63	TEMP
J	−25	KTOT
B	0.007	SUM

Binary Character Codes

CHARACTER	ASCII	EBCDIC
A	1000001	11000001
H	1001000	11001000
Y	1011001	11101000
3	0110011	11110011
+	0101011	01001110
$	0100100	01011011
=	0111101	01111110

CONSTANT	LENGTH
'SENSOR 23'	9 characters
'TIME AND DISTANCE'	17 characters
' $ AMT.'	7 characters
' '	2 characters
'08:40-13:25'	11 characters
''''''	2 characters

Partial Collating Sequences for Characters

ASCII

ｂ " # $ % & ( ) * + , − . /

0 1 2 3 4 5 6 7 8 9

: ; = ? @

A B C D E F G H I J K L M N O P Q R S T U V W X Y Z

EBCDIC

ｂ . (+ & $ *) ; − / , % ? : # @ = "

A B C D E F G H I J K L M N O P Q R S T U V W X Y Z

0 1 2 3 4 5 6 7 8 9

```
OPEN (UNIT=integer expression,
       FILE=character expression,
       ACCESS=character expression,
       STATUS=character expression,
       FORM=character expression,
       IOSTAT=integer variable,
       RECL=integer expression,
       BLANK=character expression,
       ERR=integer statement reference)
```

Inquiry Specifiers

Inquiry Specifier	Variable Type	Value for File Inquiry	Value for Unit Inquiry
ACCESS =	character	'SEQUENTIAL' 'DIRECT'	'SEQUENTIAL' 'DIRECT'
BLANK =	character	'NULL' 'ZERO'	'NULL' 'ZERO'
DIRECT =	character	'YES' 'NO' 'UNKNOWN'	—
ERR =	integer	statement number of error routine	statement number of error routine
EXIST =	logical	.TRUE. .FALSE.	.TRUE. .FALSE.
FORM =	character	'FORMATTED' 'UNFORMATTED'	'FORMATTED' 'UNFORMATTED'
FORMATTED =	character	'YES' 'NO' 'UNKNOWN'	—
IOSTAT =	integer	error code	error code
NAME =	character	—	name of the file if it is not a scratch file
NAMED† =	logical	—	.TRUE. .FALSE.
NEXTREC =	integer	next record number in direct-access file	next record number in direct-access file
NUMBER† =	integer	unit number	—
OPENED =	logical	.TRUE. .FALSE.	.TRUE. .FALSE.
RECL =	integer	record length	record length
SEQUENTIAL =	character	'YES' 'NO' 'UNKNOWN'	—
UNFORMATTED =	character	'YES' 'NO' 'UNKNOWN'	—

† These specifiers do not refer to scratch files.

ADDING FROM TOP

$$
\begin{array}{r}
0.0336 \\
+\ 0.0356 \\
\hline
0.0692 \\
+\ 0.329 \\
\hline
0.398 \\
+\ 0.519 \\
\hline
0.917
\end{array}
$$

ADDING FROM BOTTOM

$$
\begin{array}{r}
0.519 \\
+\ 0.329 \\
\hline
0.848 \\
+\ 0.0356 \\
\hline
0.883 \\
+\ 0.0336 \\
\hline
0.916
\end{array}
$$

$$a + b + (c - d)$$

$$
\begin{aligned}
0.919 + 0.829 &= 1.74 \\
0.0356 - 0.0330 &= \underline{0.00260} \\
&\ 1.74
\end{aligned}
$$

$$(a + c) + (b - d)$$

$$
\begin{aligned}
0.919 + 0.0356 &= 0.954 \\
0.829 - 0.0330 &= \underline{0.796} \\
&\ 1.75
\end{aligned}
$$

LOAD	LENGTH
0.28	6.62
0.50	5.93
0.67	4.46
0.93	4.25
1.15	3.30
1.38	3.15
1.60	2.43
1.98	1.46

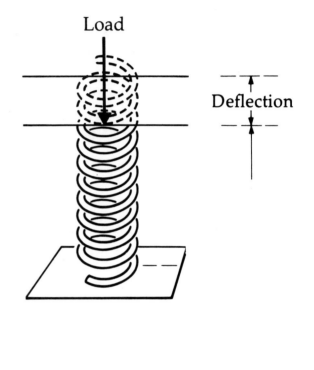

Load

Deflection

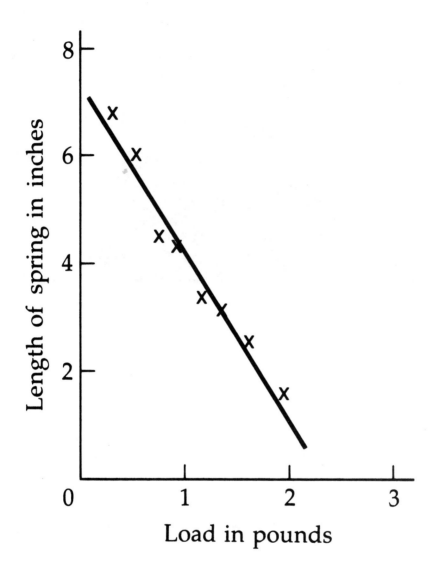

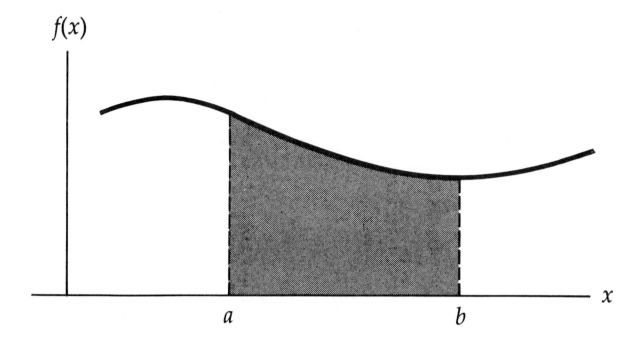

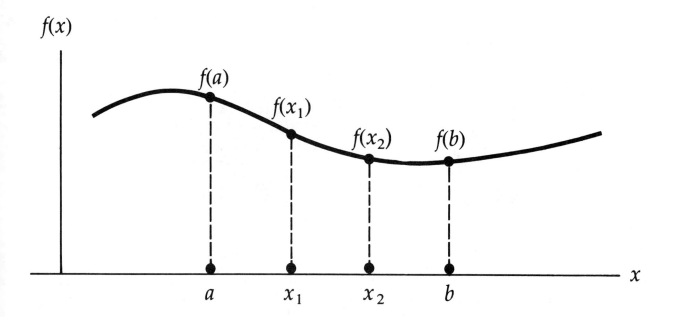

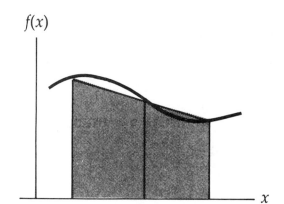 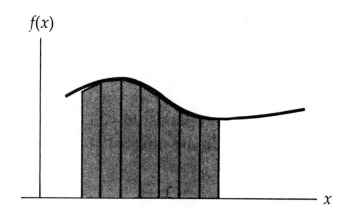

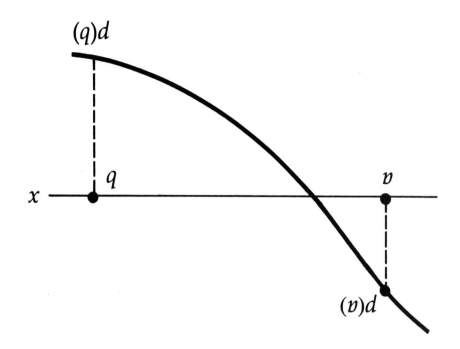

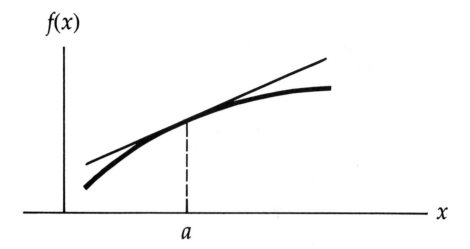

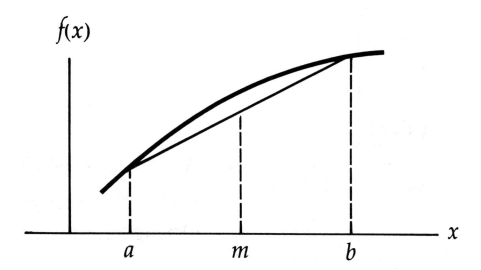

All three variables share the same storage location.

CHAPTER 5 - ADDITIONAL COMPUTER PROJECTS AND SOLUTIONS

This chapter contains new computer projects to supplement those included at the end of each chapter. For each of the following projects, we indicate the chapters in the text that need to be covered before assigning the project. We also include data files if they are needed for the project, along with sample output and a sample solution to the project.

EQUIPMENT PERFORMANCE

The sealing of sutures is extremely critical in the suture packing industry. It's important that the packages are sealed correctly so contaminants can not enter the packages and the packages are not damaged. The object which seals the package is referred to as a sealing die. Generally, sealing dies are heated with an electric heater. For the sealing process to be a success, the sealing die is maintained at an established temperature and must contact the package with a predetermined pressure for an established time period. The time period in which the sealing die contacts the package is called dwell.

Your first engineering job is as a production engineer at Dry Seals Inc. Your very first performance review is coming up in two weeks and your supervisor has asked you to complete your first independent project before the review. The project involves changing the heater which heats the die and replacing the air cylinder which lowers the die to the package. Of course you need to check these changes and issue a report about their effects on quality control. For the particular sutures we are sealing, the following parameters have been established:

Temperature:	150.0 - 170.0 degrees C
Pressure:	60 - 70 psi
Dwell:	2.0 - 2.5 seconds

The packages will not be acceptable if all these conditions are not met. For your project you are concerned about the temperature and pressure at the die. The temperature, pressure, and dwell are automatically measured for each batch sealed during the day. The values for temperature and pressure can be found in the file PACKGE . The values in the file are the following order: BATCH CODE, TEMPERATURE, and PRESSURE. A negative batch code has been placed on the last line of the data file so you know when you reach the end of the file.

You are to read the data file and determine if the packages from a particular batch were sealed within the established parameters. If the batch was not within specifications, you must print out the batch code number and whether temperature, pressure, or both were the cause of rejection. After printing out this information, you must print out the percentage of batches that were not acceptable. In addition, print out the percentage which was rejected due to temperature and the percentage which was rejected due to pressure. This will enable you to determine if most rejections were due to pressure problems, temperature problems, or both. Print the program output in the following form:

```
                BATCHES NOT WITHIN SPECIFICATIONS

        BATCH CODE          REASON

          1891        NOT ACCEPTABLE - PRESSURE AND TEMPERATURE
          1024        NOT ACCEPTABLE - TEMPERATURE
            .    .
            .    .
            .    .


          xx.xx% OF THE BATCHES WERE NOT ACCEPTABLE
          xx.xx% OF THE BATCHES WERE NOT ACCEPTABLE DUE TO TEMPERATURE
          xx.xx% OF THE BATCHES WERE NOT ACCEPTABLE DUE TO PRESSURE
```

(If a batch is not acceptable due to both temperature and
pressure, it should be used in computing the percentage of
batches not acceptable due to temperature and also in computing
the percentage of batches not acceptable due to pressure.)

Sample Data File:

```
1234  161.2 71
4586  153.4 63
2341  168.3 61
3412  153.4 62
4123  155.6 63
2134  160.0 64
4213  161.2 65
3421  161.2 61
1342  160.0 82
1324  170.0 69
4132  155.2 68
2413  161.3 66
3241  193.4 95
4231  165.0 68
1423  168.0 61
3142  160.2 62
2314  170.3 63
5678  149.9 59
8567  157.2 66
7856  153.6 68
6785  167.2 70
2345  160.0 60
5234  160.0 65
4523  170.0 70
3452  170.0 64
2349  161.2 67
-23   160.0 65
```

Desired Output Using Sample Data File:

BATCHES NOT WITHIN SPECIFICATIONS

    BATCH CODE   REASON

    1234   NOT ACCEPTABLE - PRESSURE
    1342   NOT ACCEPTABLE - PRESSURE
    3241   NOT ACCEPTABLE - TEMPERATURE AND PRESSURE
    2314   NOT ACCEPTABLE - TEMPERATURE
    5678   NOT ACCEPTABLE - TEMPERATURE AND PRESSURE

  19.23% OF THE BATCHES WERE NOT ACCEPTABLE
  11.54% OF THE BATCHES WERE NOT ACCEPTABLE DUE TO INCORRECT TEMPERATURES
  15.38% OF THE BATCHES WERE NOT ACCEPTABLE DUE TO INCORRECT PRESSURES

FORTRAN Solution:

```
*------------------------------------------------------------------*
      PROGRAM  SEAL
*
*
* PACKAGE SEALING PROBLEM
*
*
* This program reads pressure and temperature information from
* a data file and determines if the sealing process is within
* specifications.
*
      REAL PPERC, TPERC, PERC, TEMP
      INTEGER PCOUNT, TCOUNT, COUNT, PRESS, CODE, REJECT
*
* Print headings
*
      PRINT 10
 10   FORMAT(////17X, 'BATCHES NOT WITHIN SPECIFICATIONS',
     &        ///5X, 'BATCH CODE', 25X, 'REASON'//)
*
* Read values from first line in data file
*
      READ *, CODE, TEMP, PRESS
*
* Initialize counters
*
      PCOUNT = 0
      TCOUNT = 0
      COUNT = 0
      REJECT = 0
*
* Begin while loop
```

```
*
 20    IF(CODE .GT. 0) THEN
*
* Check the pressure and temperature parameters to see if
* they are within specifications.  If the batches are not
* within specifications increment REJECT by one.  If the
* rejection is due to pressure, increment PCOUNT by one.
* If the rejection is due to temperature, increment TCOUNT
* by one.  Print results.
*
         IF((TEMP .LT. 150.0 .OR. TEMP .GT. 170.0) .AND.
     &      (PRESS .LT. 60 .OR. PRESS .GT. 70)) THEN
         PRINT 30, CODE
 30      FORMAT(8X,I4,22x,'NOT ACCEPTABLE - TEMPERATURE',
     &            ' AND PRESSURE')
         REJECT = REJECT + 1
         PCOUNT = PCOUNT + 1
         TCOUNT = TCOUNT + 1
         ELSEIF(TEMP .LT. 150.0 .OR. TEMP .GT. 170.0) THEN
         PRINT 40, CODE
 40      FORMAT(8X, I4, 22x, 'NOT ACCEPTABLE - TEMPERATURE')
         REJECT = REJECT + 1
         TCOUNT = TCOUNT + 1
         ELSEIF(PRESS .LT. 60 .OR. PRESS .GT. 70) THEN
         PRINT 50, CODE
 50      FORMAT(8X, I4, 22x, 'NOT ACCEPTABLE - PRESSURE')
         REJECT = REJECT + 1
         PCOUNT = PCOUNT + 1
         ENDIF
      COUNT = COUNT + 1
      READ *, CODE, TEMP, PRESS
      GO TO 20
      ENDIF
*
* Calculate and print percentages
*
      PERC = REAL(REJECT)/REAL(COUNT)*100.0
      PPERC = REAL(PCOUNT)/REAL(COUNT)*100.0
      TPERC = REAL(TCOUNT)/REAL(COUNT)*100.0
*
      PRINT 60, PERC
 60   FORMAT(//5X, F5.2, '% OF THE BATCHES WERE NOT ACCEPTABLE')
*
      PRINT 70, TPERC
 70   FORMAT(5X, F5.2, '% OF THE BATCHES WERE NOT ACCEPTABLE',
     &          ' DUE TO INCORRECT TEMPERATURES')
*
      PRINT 80, PPERC
 80   FORMAT(5X, F5.2, '% OF THE BATCHES WERE NOT ACCEPTABLE',
     &          ' DUE TO INCORRECT PRESSURES')
*
      END
*-------------------------------------------------------------------
```

WASTE WATER TREATMENT

Organic material in waste water from industrial plants decomposes through chemical and bacterial action. Oxygen is consumed in this process as carbon dioxide and water are produced. As the oxygen is consumed, the waste water is deoxygenated. A standard procedure for determining the rate of deoxygenation begins by diluting a waste water sample with fresh water containing a known amount of dissolved oxygen. The combined sample is then held at 20 degrees C for 5 days and then checked for the amount of final oxygen. A biological oxygen demand (BOD) is then calculated from the initial and final oxygen levels. The biological oxygen demand for a 20 day test (at 20 degrees C) is called the first-stage demand. It can be calculated using the five day (BOD) measurements.

When waste water is discharged into a stream, oxygen for the process is consumed from the stream. This occurs as the organic material in the discharge decomposes. Oxygen is also continuously being absorbed into the stream from the air. These two processes, deoxygenation and reoxygenation, take place at different rates. The rate of each depends on the oxygen level in the combined mixture of waste water and stream. Initially, the rate of deoxygenation is rapid as there is a large amount of oxygen in the mixture. For this same reason, the rate of reoxygenation is slow. As oxygen is consumed in decomposing the organic material, the oxygen level of the mixture drops. The lower oxygen level in the mixture causes the deoxygenation rate to decrease. It also causes the reoxygenation rate to increase. Hence, the dissolved oxygen level in the mixture decreases with time, reaches a minimum, and then increases. As the dissolved oxygen level decreases below the normal oxygen level of the stream, an oxygen deficit in the mixture is said to occur. The oxygen deficit of the mixture can be calculated in the following manner:

First calculate the biological oxygen demand for the mixture of the stream and the waste water discharge.

$$BODmix = \frac{BODs * Qs + BODd * Qd}{Qs + Qd}$$

where   BODs is the biological oxygen demand of the stream
         BODd is the biological oxygen demand of the discharge
         Qs is the stream flow rate in million gallons/day
         Qd is the discharge flow rate in million gallons/day

Next, estimate the first stage demand at the mixture temperature, Tmix (in degrees C), using the following formula:

$$FSmix = \frac{BODmix}{0.68} * \left[(0.02 * Tmix) + 0.6\right]$$

Finally, calculate the oxygen deficit as a function of time with the equation:

$$DEFCT = \left\{\frac{Kd * FSmix}{Kr - Kd} * \left[10^{-Kd*t} - 10^{-Kr*t}\right]\right\} + \left[Do * 10^{-Kr*t}\right]$$

where Kd is the coefficient of deoxygenation
       Kr is the coefficient of reoxygenation
       Do is the initial oxygen deficit
       t is the elapsed time in days

Kd can be estimated by:

$$Kd = 0.1 * 1.047^{(Tmix-20)}$$

You have been hired as a private consultant to a new water analysis laboratory. The laboratory, Clear View Unlimited, is very busy and your contract is to write a FORTRAN program to calculate the oxygen deficit as a function of time for several streams being analyzed. The information for the streams is stored in a file called STREAMS. The value in the first data line contains the value for the number of streams in the file. Then each subsequent data line contains the information for one stream in the following order: Qd, Qs, BODd, BODs, Tmix, Kr, and Do. (All these data values are in the units mentioned above.) Your program should calculate the oxygen deficit for each stream in the file over a four day period using 0.1 day increments. It should find the maximum deficit and when it occurred. Additionally it should find the maximum deficit for all the streams in the file and remember which stream it occurred in. Make all the loops in your program DO loops with integer indices. Do not use any while loops. Additionally, your program should be written to handle any number of streams in the file. The output from your program should be in the following form:

OXYGEN DEFICIT ANALYSIS OF WASTE WATER DISCHARGE STREAMS

OXYGEN DEFICIT OF MIXTURE NO. 1

DAYS	DEFICIT
0.1	X.XXX
0.2	X.XXX
.	"
.	.
4.0	X.XXX

MAXIMUM DEFICIT OF X.XXX OCCURRED AT DAY X.X

Place the following line below the final table of values:

MAXIMUM DEFICIT OCCURED IN MIXTURE NO. XX

Sample Data File STREAMS:

```
4
002.5 065.0 000.1 015.0 017.6 00.45 07.3
005.0 108.0 002.5 023.0 012.5 01.85 02.5
023.9 003.5 000.0 145.0 017.6 00.20 01.3
005.0 108.0 002.5 000.5 020.5 00.20 02.3
```

Desired Output Using Sample Data File:

OXYGEN DEFICIT ANALYSIS OF WASTE WATER DISCHARGE STREAMS

OXYGEN DEFICIT OF MIXTURE NO. 1

DAYS	DEFICIT
0.1	6.974
0.2	6.671
0.3	6.391
0.4	6.131
0.5	5.888
0.6	5.662
0.7	5.451
0.8	5.254
0.9	5.070
1.0	4.896
1.1	4.733
1.2	4.580
1.3	4.435
1.4	4.299

1.5	4.169
1.6	4.047
1.7	3.930
1.8	3.820
1.9	3.714
2.0	3.614
2.1	3.518
2.2	3.426
2.3	3.338
2.4	3.253
2.5	3.172
2.6	3.094
2.7	3.019
2.8	2.946
2.9	2.876
3.0	2.809
3.1	2.744
3.2	2.681
3.3	2.619
3.4	2.560
3.5	2.503
3.6	2.447
3.7	2.393
3.8	2.340
3.9	2.289
4.0	2.239

MAXIMUM DEFICIT OF 6.974 OCCURED AT DAY 0.1

OXYGEN DEFICIT OF MIXTURE NO. 2

DAYS	DEFICIT
0.1	1.997
0.2	1.662
0.3	1.437
0.4	1.285
0.5	1.180
0.6	1.106
0.7	1.052
0.8	1.012
0.9	0.980
1.0	0.954
1.1	0.932
1.2	0.913
1.3	0.895
1.4	0.879
1.5	0.863
1.6	0.849
1.7	0.834
1.8	0.821
1.9	0.807
2.0	0.794
2.1	0.781
2.2	0.768

64

2.3	0.756
2.4	0.744
2.5	0.732
2.6	0.720
2.7	0.708
2.8	0.697
2.9	0.685
3.0	0.674
3.1	0.663
3.2	0.653
3.3	0.642
3.4	0.632
3.5	0.621
3.6	0.611
3.7	0.601
3.8	0.592
3.9	0.582
4.0	0.573

MAXIMUM DEFICIT OF 1.997 OCCURED AT DAY 0.1

OXYGEN DEFICIT OF MIXTURE NO. 3

DAYS	DEFICIT
0.1	1.759
0.2	2.186
0.3	2.584
0.4	2.954
0.5	3.297
0.6	3.616
0.7	3.910
0.8	4.182
0.9	4.432
1.0	4.662
1.1	4.873
1.2	5.066
1.3	5.242
1.4	5.402
1.5	5.546
1.6	5.676
1.7	5.792
1.8	5.896
1.9	5.987
2.0	6.068
2.1	6.137
2.2	6.196
2.3	6.246
2.4	6.287
2.5	6.319
2.6	6.343
2.7	6.361
2.8	6.371
2.9	6.374
3.0	6.372

```
                 3.1        6.364
                 3.2        6.350
                 3.3        6.332
                 3.4        6.309
                 3.5        6.281
                 3.6        6.250
                 3.7        6.215
                 3.8        6.176
                 3.9        6.134
                 4.0        6.090
```

MAXIMUM DEFICIT OF 6.374 OCCURED AT DAY 2.9

OXYGEN DEFICIT OF MIXTURE NO. 4

```
             DAYS        DEFICIT
             0.1        2.216
             0.2        2.136
             0.3        2.059
             0.4        1.985
             0.5        1.914
             0.6        1.845
             0.7        1.779
             0.8        1.716
             0.9        1.655
             1.0        1.597
             1.1        1.541
             1.2        1.487
             1.3        1.435
             1.4        1.385
             1.5        1.337
             1.6        1.291
             1.7        1.246
             1.8        1.203
             1.9        1.162
             2.0        1.123
             2.1        1.085
             2.2        1.048
             2.3        1.013
             2.4        0.979
             2.5        0.946
             2.6        0.914
             2.7        0.884
             2.8        0.855
             2.9        0.826
             3.0        0.799
             3.1        0.773
             3.2        0.748
             3.3        0.724
             3.4        0.700
             3.5        0.678
             3.6        0.656
             3.7        0.635
             3.8        0.615
```

```
              3.9          0.595
              4.0          0.576


         MAXIMUM DEFICIT OF 2.216 OCCURED AT DAY 0.1


         MAXIMUM DEFICIT OCCURED IN MIXTURE NO.   1




FORTRAN Solution:

*----------------------------------------------------------*
      PROGRAM  WASTE
*
*     Waste water treatment problem.
*
*

      REAL KR,KD,BODS,BODD,QS,QD,TMIX,T,BODMIX,FSMIX,DO
      REAL DEFCT, D1, D2, D3, MAXDF, MAXGND, MAXTIM
*
      INTEGER I, J, NUMSTM, MAXMIX
*
*     Write headings for top of table.
*
      PRINT 10
   10 FORMAT (1X, 15X, 'OXYGEN DEFICIT ANALYSIS OF WASTE WATER ',
     &          'DISCHARGE STREAMS')
*
*     Zero out maximum deficit value for all streams.
*
      MAXGND = 0.0
*
*     Read in first value to find out how many stream mixtures
*     are in the STREAM file.
*
      READ  *, NUMSTM
*
      DO 200 I = 1, NUMSTM
*
*     Write heading for this stream mixture.
*
          PRINT 20, I
   20     FORMAT (/1X, 15X, 14X, 'OXYGEN DEFICIT OF MIXTURE NO. ',
     &          I2, //1X, 15X, 17X, 'DAYS', 8X, 'DEFICIT', /1X)
*
*     Zero out maximum deficit for this stream mixture.
*
          MAXDF = 0.0
*
*     Read in data for the stream.
*
          READ *, QD, QS, BODD, BODS, TMIX, KR, DO
*
```

67

```
*        Calculate mixture parameters.
*
      BODMIX = ((BODS * QS) + (BODD * QD))/(QS + QD)
      FSMIX = BODMIX * (0.02 * TMIX + 0.6)/ 0.68
      KD = 0.1 * 1.047 ** (TMIX - 20.0)
*
*        Calculate the deficit for the four day period.
*
      DO 100 J = 1, 40
          T = REAL(J)/10.0
          D1 = (KD * FSMIX) / (KR - KD)
          D2 = 10.0 ** (-KD * T) - 10.0 ** (-KR * T)
          D3 = DO * 10.0 ** (-KR * T)
          DEFCT = (D1 * D2) + D3
          PRINT 30, T, DEFCT
   30        FORMAT (1X, 15X, 18X, F3.1, 9X, F5.3)
          IF (DEFCT .GT. MAXDF) THEN
              MAXDF = DEFCT
              MAXTIM = T
              IF (MAXDF .GT. MAXGND) THEN
                  MAXGND = MAXDF
                  MAXMIX = I
              ENDIF
          ENDIF
  100      CONTINUE
*
*     Print out maximum deficit of this stream.
*
          PRINT 110, MAXDF, MAXTIM
  110        FORMAT (/1X, 15X, 5X, 'MAXIMUM DEFICIT OF ',
     &                 F5.3, ' OCCURED AT DAY ', F3.1, /1X)
*
*     End outer loop for all the stream mixtures.
*
  200 CONTINUE
*
*     Print out which stream had the maximum deficit.
*
      PRINT 210, MAXMIX
  210 FORMAT( /1X, 15X, 6X, 'MAXIMUM DEFICIT OCCURED IN ',
     &           'MIXTURE NO. ', I2)
*
      STOP
      END
*----------------------------------------------------------------*
```

Additional Project - Chapter 5

NASA'S EXPERIMENTAL DIETS

NASA has been sending animals into space for over twenty-five years and they have always experienced problems with feeding and maintaining these experimental animals during space flight. Recently, a directive was sent out from NASA's Biological Sciences Department and from Bionetics (a general contractor) elaborating on the problems associated with micro-gravity experimentation and calling for the solution of these problems. You are part of the DDT (Diet Development Team) whose task it is to test twenty different animal diets and evaluate them according to how well they meet the following criteria. The result of this evaluation will be the selection of the single best, overall diet that will be used in space. The criteria for the evaluation is as follows:

1.   Cost (The less expensive the better, although you do not want to sacrifice quality for cost.)

2.   Nutritional Adequacy (Does the diet supply the animals with the nutrition they require to maintain normal body function?)

3.   Ease of Operation (Does the food and the packaging require a significant amount of time for the shuttle crew to prepare?)

4.   Supplier Cooperation (Will the supplier of the food mixture be willing to deliver the product upon demand?)

5.   Palatability (Will the animals eat it?)

6.   Data Collection (Will the diet allow the scientist to gather sufficient data about the animals' feeding habits and activities?)

7.   Risk (Does the diet present any health or safety-related problems to the crew?)

8.   Water (Does the diet supply the animals with enough water so that extra water supplies do not have to be sent along with the animals?)

Each criteria was ranked on a scale from one to nine. A value of nine is the best and indicates low cost and risk but high nutrition, ease of operation, supplier cooperation, palatability, data collection capabilities and water content. Your job is to take the ranked values and calculate an overall score. The overall score will be computed to account for some criteria being more important than others. The best diet will be the one with the highest score after using the scaled equations at the end of this discussion. It is your task as the Biomedical Engineer of the DDT to collect the scientists' findings from the actual testing of the diets and determine the scores of the twenty diets, which diet was best (had the highest scores), which diet was worst (lowest score) and what was the percent difference between the best and worst scores.

You will need to follow certain criteria yourself as you compete this program. First, the data is located in the file NASA. The data file is set up with twenty rows (one for each diet) and eight columns (one for each criteria). Use an OPEN statement in your FORTRAN program to read in the data. Additionally, use the END parameter in your read statement even though you already know that you are testing twenty diets. You are writing a general program which might be used at another time with more (or less) than twenty diets. Therefore, do not use a do loop in your program to compute the scores for each diet. Instead use a standard while loop for input and analysis of the data. Second, note that no score is greater than one hundred or less than zero. Third, your output should be centered on the printed page. Print out a summary section and then the score for each diet. It should look similar to this:

RESULTS FOR EXPERIMENTAL SPACE DIET

THE BEST DIET HAD A SCORE OF **.***
THE WORST DIET HAD A SCORE OF **.***
THE PERCENT DIFFERENCE BETWEEN THE BEST AND WORST DIETS WAS **.**

```
            DIET   SCORE
            1.     XX.XX
            2.     XX.XX
            3.       .
            4.       .
            .        .
            .        .
```

Fourth, there was a little problem that was discovered concerning criteria five. It seems that some of the scientists were a bit concerned with some diets receiving low scores because of low values given to palatability. Consequently, it was agreed upon to multiply the criteria five equation by 1.47 if the value for palatability for the diet being computed was less than or equal to two.

Here are the equations you should use for the different criteria. Note that each has been scaled for you with regard to its relative importance to NASA's specifications.

$$score_1 = 1.984 \log_{10} val_1 + \frac{3.968 * val_1}{val_1 + 1}$$

$$score_2 = 0.1987 \sqrt{(val_2^2 + 16.543) * 14.88 \, val_2}$$

$$score_3 = val_3^{1/3} \qquad\qquad score_4 = e^{\left(\frac{val_4 + 2.443}{2.2 \, val_4 + 1.25}\right)}$$

$$score_5 = 0.1851 + \sqrt{val_5} \qquad\qquad score_6 = \frac{\sqrt{val_6^2 - 2 \, val_6} - val_6}{0.2}$$

$$score_7 = 1.889 \, val_7 \qquad\qquad score_8 = val_8 + 3.406$$

Sample Data File:

```
6  8  3  3  9  9  1  4
8  3  2  6  7  7  4  6
5  5  5  3  7  2  8  9
8  5  3  1  2  7  5  3
9  9  2  2  7  5  1  9
8  8  3  3  3  8  9  8
9  9  2  1  4  7  8  9
4  2  1  4  5  8  4  3
9  8  7  6  5  4  3  2
5  9  4  3  2  6  8  7
9  9  9  9  5  9  9  9
8  8  8  8  6  8  8  8
8  9  8  9  8  9  8  9
5  7  9  7  5  7  9  7
6  8  6  4  6  8  6  8
2  1  2  1  4  6  2  4
9  9  9  9  2  9  9  9
6  6  6  6  6  6  6  6
3  7  1  8  2  9  3  9
7  1  8  2  9  3  9  4
```

71

Desired Output Using Sample Data File:

RESULTS FOR EXPERIMENTAL SPACE DIET

THE BEST DIET HAS THE SCORE OF 58.491
THE WORST DIET HAS THE SCORE OF 18.290
THE PERCENT DIFFERENCE BETWEEN THE TWO IS 68.73

DIET	SCORE
1.	35.01
2.	29.46
3.	39.80
4.	33.30
5.	43.12
6.	53.18
7.	56.43
8.	23.20
9.	36.26
10.	53.36
11.	58.49
12.	52.31
13.	56.97
14.	49.36
15.	48.13
16.	18.29
17.	58.42
18.	40.03
19.	38.19
20.	33.81

FORTRAN Solution:

```
*-------------------------------------------------------------------*
       PROGRAM  DIET
*
* This program is designed to read values from an existing  data
* file and manipulate the data so as to find the best and the
* worst diets.   The diets are judged on their ability to satisfy
* the criteria presented in the assignment sheet with a score of
* nine being the best possible and one being the worst.   This
* program will then give a print-out of all the scores and then
* list the best diet, the worst diet, and the percent difference
* between the best and the worst diets.
*
***** initialize variables ******
*
       REAL VAL(8), SCORES(8), SMDIET(100), MAX, MIN, DIFF, PI
       INTEGER I,J,L
       DATA PI,I,MAX,MIN /3.141593,1,0.0,100.0/
*
*
```

```
***** open and read data file ********
*
        OPEN(UNIT=12, FILE='NASA',STATUS='OLD')
*
  5     READ (12,*,END = 10) (VAL(J), J = 1,8)
*
*
***** equations for determining acceptability *******
*
            SCORES(1) = 1.984 * ALOG10(VAL(1))
     &            + (( 3.968 * VAL(1)) / (VAL(1) + 1.0))
*
            SCORES(2) = 0.1987 * SQRT( (VAL(2)**2 + 16.543)
     &            * 14.88 * VAL(2))
*
            SCORES(3) = VAL(3) ** (1.0/3.0)
*
            SCORES(4) = EXP((VAL(4)+2.443)/(2.2*VAL(4)+1.25))
*
            SCORES(5) = 0.1851 + SQRT (VAL(5))
            IF(VAL(5).LE.2.0) SCORES(5) = 1.47 * SCORES(5)
*
            SCORES(6) = (SQRT(VAL(6)**2 - 2.0 * VAL(6) )
     &            - VAL(6))/0.2
*
            SCORES(7) = 1.889*VAL(7)
*
            SCORES(8) = VAL(8) + 3.406
*
*
******** sum the values for each diet ***************
*
            SMDIET(I) = 0.0
            DO 7 J = 1, 8
                SMDIET(I) = SMDIET(I) + SCORES(J)
  7         CONTINUE
*
            I = I + 1
            GO TO 5
*
*
******** print headers ****************************
*
 10     PRINT 120
 120    FORMAT(14X,'RESULTS FOR EXPERIMENTAL SPACE DIET',/)
*
*
******* find the best and worst diets ***************
******* along with their % difference ***************
*
        DO 170 L = 1, I - 1
            IF(SMDIET(L).GT.MAX)MAX=SMDIET(L)
*
            IF(SMDIET(L).LT.MIN)MIN=SMDIET(L)
 170    CONTINUE
```

```
*
          DIFF = ((MAX-MIN)/MAX)*100.0
*
*
****** print results *********************************
*
      PRINT *
      PRINT 230, MAX
 230  FORMAT(13X,'THE BEST DIET HAS THE SCORE OF ',F6.3,)
      PRINT 240, MIN
 240  FORMAT(13X,'THE WORST DIET HAS THE SCORE OF ',F6.3,)
      PRINT 250, DIFF
 250  FORMAT(8X,'THE PERCENT DIFFERENCE BETWEEN THE TWO IS ',
     +         F5.2,)
*
      PRINT 165
 165  FORMAT (//25X, 'DIET', 4X, 'SCORE')
      DP 220 L = 1,20
          PRINT 200, L, SMDIET(L)
 200      FORMAT(25X,I2, '.', 5X, F5.2)
 220  CONTINUE
*
*
*************************************************************
*
      END
*------------------------------------------------------------*
```

PROJECT MANAGEMENT

   The timely use of resources is important to the success of
any engineering project.   This is often achieved by using a
critical   path analysis of a project.   One method for this
analysis   starts by breaking up a project into various sequential
events.   Then each event is broken down into various tasks.
Although one event must be completed before the next one is
started,   various tasks within an event can occur at the same
time.   Thus the time it takes to complete an event depends on the
number of days required to finish the longest task.   Similarly,
the   total time it takes to finish a project is the sum of the
time it takes to finish each event.

   Your boss has just asked you to write a program in FORTRAN
to analyze the critical path for a multimillion dollar project.
Your company was low bidder on the project and would have been
awarded the contract, but your project timetable was 3 weeks
slower than your closest competitor, Low-Bal Projects Unlimited.
Your boss wants to investigate several different ways of reducing
the project time by using your FORTRAN program.

   Your program will first read all the information for the
current data base into a two dimensional integer array.   The
array will contain three columns, one for the event number,
another for the task number, and the last for the number of days
it takes to complete the task.   (Assume there will never be more
than 100 task-events placed in the array.) This data base is
stored in the file OLDBASE.   Each line (record) in the
file contains one row of information for the array.   The data in
the file is stored in the same order as above.   The file is
already sorted by events, so that all the task-events for event
No. 3 occur before any of those for event No. 4, for example.
However, the tasks for an event may not necessarily be in
sequential order.

   Next your program should open the file CHANGES.   Each line
in this file is one of the changes to be made to the project data
base.   The records in the file are set up in the same format as
the those in the CHANGES file. Write a subroutine that is called
in the main program to change the number of days to finish a
particular task-event.   The subroutine should be called with the
following statement in the main program:

          CALL CHANGE (PROJ, EVENT, TASK, DAYS)

where PROJ is the array containing the data base information.
The other integer arguments are self explanatory.   If the
particular task-event in the change file does not exist in the
data base, your subroutine should prints an error message in the
following form:

```
              EVENT XX  TASK NO. XXX DOES NOT EXIST
           NOT POSSIBLE TO MAKE CHANGES TO THIS ENTRY
```

Use this subroutine to process all the entries in the file. (There are no trailer signals in any of the input files. Use the END parameter in the READ statement to form a valid WHILE loop structure for processing all the records in the change file.)

After your program has processed the CHANGE file, it should determine the new total number of days it takes to complete the project. Write a function to determine the maximum number of days for all the tasks within an event. Thus the function will check all the tasks for a specified event and determine the maximum number of days to complete any of these. The functions will be invoked in the main program with the following reference:

```
            variable = MAXDAY (PROJ, EVENT)
```

where PROJ is the same as above, and EVENT is the event the function should be checking. Write out a report (from the main program) to display the maximum number of days for each event and then the total number of days to complete the project. The report should be in the following form:

```
        EVENT NO.        TIME FOR COMPLETION
        ---------        -------------------

            1            X WEEK(S) X DAYS
            2            X WEEK(S) X DAYS
            .                .         .
            .                .         .
            XX           X WEEK(S) X DAYS
        ---------        -------------------

          TOTAL          XX WEEKS  X DAYS
```

(Note: use 5 days per week to determine the number of weeks in the above table. Additionally, your program should use the noun WEEK instead of WEEKS if there is only one week in the time for completion of a particular event.)

Finally, write the modified data base out to a new file called NEWBASE.

Sample Data File OLDBASE

```
1   100    3
1   105    8
1   107    6
1   108    9
1   502   11
1   431   13
1   597    6
2   100    3
2   105    6
2   500    3
2   660    1
2   754    4
3   101    3
3   105    8
3   321   18
3   495   11
3   708   18
4   100    5
4   105    8
5   000   12
6   100    5
6   500    4
6   502    2
6   648    2
6   700    3
```

Sample Data FIle CHANGES

```
1 105    5
1 108    8
1 431   15
2 101    4
2 500    4
2 745    8
3 101    2
4 105    7
6 648    3
6 500    6
```

Desired Output Using Sample Data File:

```
                  EVENT  2 TASK NO. 101 DOES NOT EXIST
           NOT POSSIBLE TO MAKE CHANGES IN THIS ENTRY

                  EVENT  2 TASK NO. 745 DOES NOT EXIST
           NOT POSSIBLE TO MAKE CHANGES IN THIS ENTRY




              PROJECT COMPLETION TIMETABLE
              EVENT NO.    TIME FOR COMPLETION
              ---------    --------------------


                  1        3 WEEKS 0 DAYS
                  2        1 WEEK  1 DAYS
                  3        3 WEEKS 3 DAYS
                  4        1 WEEK  2 DAYS
                  5        2 WEEKS 2 DAYS
                  6        1 WEEK  1 DAYS
              ---------    --------------------

                TOTAL      12 WEEKS 4 DAYS
```

FORTRAN Solution:

```
*------------------------------------------------------------------*
*
*
      PROGRAM FP6
*
*     This program reads in a data base of project scheduling
*     information from a file, then reads in changes to the
*     scheduling array, and finally, calculates the minimum
*     project length
*
      INTEGER PROJ(101, 3), EVENT, TASK, DAYS,
     &        TOTALD, WEEKS, MAXDAY, LSTEVT
      INTEGER I, J
*
      DATA I, TOTALD /1, 0/
*
*     Open file of data base information and read into the array
*     also open up the file of changes at same time.
*
      OPEN (UNIT = 2, FILE = 'OLDBASE', STATUS = 'OLD')
      OPEN (UNIT = 3, FILE = 'CHANGES', STATUS = 'OLD')
*
*     Read in data keeping track of end of data.
*
   10 READ(2, *, END = 20) (PROJ(I, J), J = 1, 3)
```

78

```
          I = I + 1
          GO TO 10
*
*    Mark the last valid row in the array with
*    a -999 in the subsequent row (column 1 for event).
*
  20 PROJ(I, 1) = -999
*
*    Save last event number.
*
     LSTEVT = PROJ (I - 1, 1)
*
*    Start processing changes.
*
  30 READ (3, *, END = 40) EVENT, TASK, DAYS
     CALL CHANGE (PROJ, EVENT, TASK, DAYS)
     GO TO 30
*
*    Now find new total project length.
*
  40 CONTINUE
*
*        Print headings.
*
     PRINT 50
  50 FORMAT (///1X, 16X, 'PROJECT COMPLETION TIMETABLE',
    &        /1X, 14X, 'EVENT NO.', 4X, 'TIME FOR COMPLETION',
    &        /1X, 14X, '---------', 4X, '--------------------',
    &        /1X )
*
     DO 80 EVENT = 1, LSTEVT
          DAYS = MAXDAY (PROJ, EVENT)
          TOTALD = TOTALD + DAYS
          WEEKS = DAYS / 5
          IF (WEEKS .EQ. 1) THEN
                PRINT 60, EVENT, WEEKS, MOD(DAYS, 5)
  60            FORMAT (1X, 16X, I2, 11X, I1, ' WEEK  ',
    &                   I1, ' DAYS')
          ELSE
                PRINT 70, EVENT, WEEKS, MOD(DAYS, 5)
  70            FORMAT (1X, 16X, I2, 11X, I1, ' WEEKS ',
    &                   I1, ' DAYS')
          ENDIF
  80 CONTINUE
*
*    Print total time.
*
     WEEKS = TOTALD / 5
     PRINT 90, WEEKS, MOD(TOTALD, 5)
  90 FORMAT (1X, 14X, '---------', 4X, '--------------------',
    &        /1X, 15X, 'TOTAL', 8X, I2, ' WEEKS ',
    &        I1, ' DAYS')
*
*    Write out the new data base.
*
```

```
            OPEN (UNIT = 4, FILE = 'NEWBASE', STATUS = 'NEW')
            I = 1
  100 IF (PROJ (I, 1) .NE. -999) THEN
            WRITE (4, *) (PROJ(I, J), J = 1, 3)
            I = I + 1
            GO TO 100
      ENDIF
*
      END
*------------------------------------------------------------
      SUBROUTINE CHANGE(PROJ, EVENT, TASK, DAYS)
*
*     This subroutine changes  the number of days of
*     an event-task in the project array.
*
      INTEGER PROJ (101, 3), EVENT, TASK, DAYS
      INTEGER I
*
*     Find location in array for specified
*     event-task (if it exists).  Use null
*     then clause to simplify logic.
*
      I = 1
   10 IF ((PROJ (I, 1) .EQ. -999) .OR.
     &     ((PROJ (I, 1) .EQ. EVENT) .AND.
     &      (PROJ (I, 2) .EQ. TASK))) THEN
      ELSE
            I = I + 1
            GO TO 10
      ENDIF
*
*     Print an error message
*     or make a change in the project array.
*
      IF (PROJ (I, 1) .EQ. -999) THEN
            PRINT 20, EVENT, TASK
   20       FORMAT (1X, 18X, 'EVENT ', I2, ' TASK NO. ',
     &              I3, ' DOES NOT EXIST', /1X, 14X,
     &              'NOT POSSIBLE TO MAKE CHANGES IN '
     &              'THIS ENTRY', /1X)
      ELSE
            PROJ (I, 3) = DAYS
      ENDIF
*
      RETURN
      END
*------------------------------------------------------------
      INTEGER FUNCTION MAXDAY (PROJ, EVENT)
*
*     This function finds the task for a
*     given event which has the maximum
*     number of days for the event.
*
      INTEGER PROJ (101, 3), EVENT
      INTEGER I
```

```
*
*       Find beginning location of desired event.
*
        I = 1
  10 IF (PROJ (I, 1) .NE. EVENT) THEN
            I = I + 1
            GO TO 10
        ENDIF
*
*       Find the maximum number of days for all
*       the tasks associated with the event.
*
        MAXDAY = 0
  20 IF (PROJ(I, 1) .EQ. EVENT) THEN
            IF (PROJ (I, 3) .GT. MAXDAY) MAXDAY = PROJ (I, 3)
            I = I + 1
            GO TO 20
        ENDIF
*
        RETURN
        END
*-------------------------------------------------------------*
```

TRAFFIC FLOW ANALYSIS

A transportation engineer can quickly analyze the flow of traffic through an intersection with the aid of a computer. For example, this can include determining average traffic flow in one direction or the hour in which the total maximum traffic flow occurs. Such information can then be used in considering changes which would improve traffic flow and lower accident rates.

Data has been collected from an Albuquerque intersection for a 16 hour period and stored in a file called CARS. The values in the file are broken into 15 minute segments and into the direction the traffic was flowing as it entered the intersection. For example, the columns in the file labeled SB indicates the columns are for south bound traffic into the intersection. The second heading for the columns is R, T, or L indicating that the incoming traffic was turning right, passing through, or turning left in the intersection.

Your job as an independent consultant to the city is to write a program in FORTRAN to perform several analyses. The program you write will be used for analyzing data from a variety of dates. Use the data provided for testing your program to make sure it works correctly.

To make it easier, an edited copy of the data file CARS has been created and is stored in the file TRAFFIC. This edited copy does not have the labels for direction of flow; therefore, look at the file CARS to determine which column in the file corresponds to which flow measurement. Additionally, the edited copy of the file does not have any of the time information in it. However, the rows in the edited file are still in the same order. Hence the first line in the file TRAFFIC is for the quarter hour period from 6:00 to 6:15 and the last for the period from 21:45 to 22:00 hours.

Begin your program by reading in all the data in the file into a two dimensional array with 13 columns and 64 rows. Each row in the array corresponds to a data line in the file and the last 12 columns correspond to the 12 values on the data line. Fill the first column with the beginning time for the quarter hour period corresponding to the data line. This should be stored in decimal hour form. For example, the second line of the file has the information for the period from 6:15 to 6:30. So the entry in column 1 of the second row would be 6.25.

Now make the following analyses. First, generate a table of the hourly flows in each direction. There should be an additional column in the table for the total flow. Additionally at the bottom of the table the average hourly flow for the 16 hour period should be printed. Write out the data in the following format. Center it carefully in the following form:

AVERAGE TRAFFIC FLOW THROUGH ALBUQUERQUE INTERSECTION

Time	Northbound	Eastbound	Southbound	Westbound	Total
6:00	xxxx	xxxx	xxxx	xxxx	xxxx
7:00	.	.	.	.	.
.	.	.	.	.	.
21:00	xxxx	xxxx	xxxx	xxxx	xxxx
Average	xxxx	xxxx	xxxx	xxxx	xxxx

Many intersections need left hand turn signals on the traffic lights to provide for the smooth flow of left turning traffic. Find the maximum number of left hand turns that occured in a quarter hour period. Print the result as:

Maximum left hand turns in a 15 minute period was XXX

Next, find the consective one hour period with the largest total traffic flow through the intersection. Note this may not necessarily begin on the hour. For example it might be the time period from 7:45 to 8:45. Print out the result as:

Maximum total flow for a one hour period began at XX.XX hrs

Since this intersection has a traffic light, the traffic is only entering the intersection in the south and north bound directions at once or in the east and west bound directions at once. (The lights only allows traffic in one orientation at a given moment.) Find the quarter hour period which had the highest flow in a particular orientation (i.e. either north-south or east-west orientatioin). Thus you must also determine which of the two orientations had the larger flow before you determine which quater hour period had the maximum flow for one of these orientations. Print out the result as:

The maximum orientated flow was XXXX and
occured in the {north-south/east-west} directions

(Your printout should only include one choice of directions)

83

Sample Data for File CARS:

Time Period	SB R	SB T	SB L	WB R	WB T	WB L	NB R	NB T	NB L	EB R	EB T	EB L
1 (6:00-6:15)	6	35	0	3	4	3	0	22	5	6	1	3
2 (6:15-6:30)	6	77	1	5	3	4	1	24	6	6	0	3
3 (6:30-6:45)	11	111	0	12	11	16	0	68	8	13	0	16
4 (6:45-7:00)	15	176	3	10	8	16	0	80	9	15	3	15
5 (7:00-7:15)	15	255	6	12	11	34	4	93	16	23	4	23
6 (7:15-7:30)	19	258	5	8	19	29	7	154	18	18	4	27
7 (7:30-7:45)	30	311	4	26	33	39	5	187	22	28	6	27
8 (7:45-8:00)	33	290	3	21	24	34	6	173	32	23	2	21
9 (8:00-8:15)	34	202	3	19	12	18	4	138	19	13	13	13
10 (8:15-8:30)	23	166	8	11	17	15	4	131	23	22	5	12
11 (8:30-8:45)	26	164	4	12	13	6	4	113	20	17	7	16
12 (8:45-9:00)	10	143	2	14	11	8	4	120	29	22	6	13
13 (9:00-9:15)	9	110	6	9	13	7	6	99	19	17	8	12
14 (9:15-9:30)	11	71	3	10	8	2	1	79	18	10	4	13
15 (9:30-9:45)	16	88	1	8	6	5	6	84	16	6	3	12
16 (9:45-10:00)	13	75	4	10	11	4	3	89	22	15	6	4
17 (10:00-10:15)	10	90	7	5	4	4	4	71	14	7	4	9
18 (10:15-10:30)	13	78	5	6	5	4	5	91	13	10	4	7
19 (10:30-10:45)	5	90	7	7	7	7	5	77	9	6	4	8
20 (10:45-11:00)	11	68	6	5	10	4	3	75	13	16	7	13
21 (11:00-11:15)	15	86	3	1	12	5	5	55	9	8	9	6
22 (11:15-11:30)	14	87	4	6	10	9	4	94	15	19	9	6
23 (11:30-11:45)	9	102	6	7	11	8	7	79	22	17	12	13
24 (11:45-12:00)	14	98	5	5	15	8	3	92	19	13	16	10
25 (12:00-12:15)	11	119	7	9	11	9	9	105	25	11	8	17
26 (12:15-12:30)	16	80	4	7	11	3	4	90	14	16	13	9
27 (12:30-12:45)	16	108	7	13	11	7	7	73	9	12	10	9
28 (12:45-13:00)	18	91	8	5	13	6	8	84	12	14	13	14
29 (13:00-13:15)	10	88	8	7	6	4	7	83	24	15	10	12
30 (13:15-13:30)	15	92	5	10	19	11	4	113	23	19	13	15
31 (13:30-13:45)	17	97	4	7	7	3	7	104	21	17	12	11
32 (13:45-14:00)	20	91	8	17	8	9	9	88	21	16	10	18
33 (14:00-14:15)	10	97	8	6	13	6	4	100	21	14	16	17
34 (14:15-14:30)	14	100	9	10	11	5	7	86	11	27	13	10
35 (14:30-14:45)	17	103	8	5	12	5	5	106	8	16	17	11
36 (14:45-15:00)	14	107	6	12	11	6	12	77	23	19	11	12
37 (15:00-15:15)	18	103	12	9	8	6	5	101	16	25	16	25
38 (15:15-15:30)	20	136	13	7	9	4	9	133	20	21	11	22
39 (15:30-15:45)	22	129	3	6	9	5	7	134	13	44	20	17
40 (15:45-16:00)	21	125	7	6	17	3	16	163	25	20	17	19
41 (16:00-16:15)	20	150	15	8	12	8	13	147	17	21	17	9
42 (16:15-16:30)	27	158	4	9	12	17	16	181	17	28	17	22
43 (16:30-16:45)	22	144	14	5	13	9	16	230	32	27	24	26
44 (16:45-17:00)	24	180	22	6	17	10	19	272	31	29	21	21
45 (17:00-17:15)	31	179	13	8	11	5	23	292	35	31	14	26
46 (17:15-17:30)	31	190	18	8	10	7	14	257	40	24	31	30
47 (17:30-17:45)	28	176	23	8	13	7	23	222	21	31	21	34
48 (17:45-18:00)	33	176	20	8	10	8	16	207	22	24	22	22
49 (18:00-18:15)	25	136	25	7	16	6	9	196	13	27	30	27
50 (18:15-18:30)	15	110	9	7	10	3	10	146	17	21	11	11
51 (18:30-18:45)	15	119	9	7	9	8	13	134	20	14	17	17

```
52 (18:45-19:00)  23  136  8   4   11  3   8   139  27  21  10  14
53 (19:00-19:15)  20  100  11  4   9   6   8   106  18  17  10  26
54 (19:15-19:30)  9   103  6   12  12  10  4   133  20  14  11  19
55 (19:30-19:45)  8   85   9   5   3   3   6   95   10  10  11  13
56 (19:45-20:00)  7   74   9   4   3   4   2   80   12  8   12  12
57 (20:00-20:15)  14  69   8   2   8   2   5   65   11  7   8   7
58 (20:15-20:30)  14  67   3   6   6   3   1   98   7   12  6   9
59 (20:30-20:45)  7   86   8   5   4   5   4   72   8   25  11  12
60 (20:45-21:00)  11  81   4   3   5   4   10  78   20  12  9   6
61 (21:00-21:15)  15  87   7   4   4   2   14  89   14  15  11  3
62 (21:15-21:30)  11  98   4   1   5   1   4   70   11  8   19  10
63 (21:30-21:45)  8   82   6   2   7   3   2   65   7   7   8   7
64 (21:45-22:00)  14  66   7   1   5   7   6   79   15  11  8   10
```

Sample Data File TRAFFIC

```
6    35   0    3    4    3    0    22   5    6    1    3
6    77   1    5    3    4    1    24   6    6    0    3
11   111  0    12   11   16   0    68   8    13   0    16
15   176  3    10   8    16   0    80   9    15   3    15
15   255  6    12   11   34   4    93   16   23   4    23
19   258  5    8    19   29   7    154  18   18   4    27
30   311  4    26   33   39   5    187  22   28   6    27
33   290  3    21   24   34   6    173  32   23   2    21
34   202  3    19   12   18   4    138  19   13   13   13
23   166  8    11   17   15   4    131  23   22   5    12
26   164  4    12   13   6    4    113  20   17   7    16
10   143  2    14   11   8    4    120  29   22   6    13
9    110  6    9    13   7    6    99   19   17   8    12
11   71   3    10   8    2    1    79   18   10   4    13
16   88   1    8    6    5    6    84   16   6    3    12
13   75   4    10   11   4    3    89   22   15   6    4
10   90   7    5    4    4    4    71   14   7    4    9
13   78   5    6    5    4    5    91   13   10   4    7
5    90   7    7    7    7    5    77   9    6    4    8
11   68   6    5    10   4    3    75   13   16   7    13
15   86   3    1    12   5    5    55   9    8    9    6
14   87   4    6    10   9    4    94   15   19   9    6
9    102  6    7    11   8    7    79   22   17   12   13
14   98   5    5    15   8    3    92   19   13   16   10
11   119  7    9    11   9    9    105  25   11   8    17
16   80   4    7    11   3    4    90   14   16   13   9
16   108  7    13   11   7    7    73   9    12   10   9
18   91   8    5    13   6    8    84   12   14   13   14
10   88   8    7    6    4    7    83   24   15   10   12
15   92   5    10   19   11   4    113  23   19   13   15
17   97   4    7    7    3    7    104  21   17   12   11
20   91   8    17   8    9    9    88   21   16   10   18
10   97   8    6    13   6    4    100  21   14   16   17
14   100  9    10   11   5    7    86   11   27   13   10
17   103  8    5    12   5    5    106  8    16   17   11
14   107  6    12   11   6    12   77   23   19   11   12
18   103  12   9    8    6    5    101  16   25   16   25
20   136  13   7    9    4    9    133  20   21   11   22
22   129  3    6    9    5    7    134  13   44   20   17
```

21	125	7	6	17	3	16	163	25	20	17	19
20	150	15	8	12	8	13	147	17	21	17	9
27	158	4	9	12	17	16	181	17	28	17	22
22	144	14	5	13	9	16	230	32	27	24	26
24	180	22	6	17	10	19	272	31	29	21	21
31	179	13	8	11	5	23	292	35	31	14	26
31	190	18	8	10	7	14	257	40	24	31	30
28	176	23	8	13	7	23	222	21	31	21	34
33	176	20	8	10	8	16	207	22	24	22	22
25	136	25	7	16	6	9	196	13	27	30	27
15	110	9	7	10	3	10	146	17	21	11	11
15	119	9	7	9	8	13	134	20	14	17	17
23	136	8	4	11	3	8	139	27	21	10	14
20	100	11	4	9	6	8	106	18	17	10	26
9	103	6	12	12	10	4	133	20	14	11	19
8	85	9	5	3	3	6	95	10	10	11	13
7	74	9	4	3	4	2	80	12	8	12	12
14	69	8	2	8	2	5	65	11	7	8	7
14	67	3	6	6	3	1	98	7	12	6	9
7	86	8	5	4	5	4	72	8	25	11	12
11	81	4	3	5	4	10	78	20	12	9	6
15	87	7	4	4	2	14	89	14	15	11	3
11	98	4	1	5	1	4	70	11	8	19	10
8	82	6	2	7	3	2	65	7	7	8	7
14	66	7	1	5	7	6	79	15	11	8	10

Desired Output Using Sample Data File

AVERAGE TRAFFIC FLOW THROUGH ALBUQUERQUE INTERSECTIONS

Time	Northbound	Eastbound	Southbound	Westbound	Total
6:00	223	81	441	95	840
7:00	717	206	1229	290	2442
8:00	609	159	785	156	1709
9:00	442	110	407	93	1052
10:00	380	95	390	68	933
11:00	404	138	443	97	1082
12:00	440	146	485	105	1176
13:00	504	168	455	108	1235
14:00	460	183	493	102	1238
15:00	642	257	609	89	1597
16:00	991	262	780	126	2159
17:00	1172	310	918	103	2503
18:00	732	220	630	91	1673
19:00	494	163	441	75	1173
20:00	379	124	372	53	928
21:00	376	117	405	42	94
Average	560	171	580	105	1417

Maximum number of left hand turns in a 15 minute period was   95
Maximum total flow for a one hour period began at 16.75 hrs

The maximum orientated flow was 573 and
occured in the north-south directions

86

FORTRAN Solution:

```
*------------------------------------------------------------------*
*
*
*        Traffic Flow Analysis
*
      REAL FLOW(64, 13), AVG(4), CNT(4), TIME, HTOTAL, LTRNS,
     &      LMAX, HMAX, FQTR, SQTR, TQTR, LQTR, SUMNS, SUMEW,
     &      MAXNS, MAXEW
      INTEGER I, J, K, L, HTIME
*
      DATA AVG, FQTR, SQTR, TQTR, LQTR /8 * 0.0/
*
      OPEN (UNIT = 2, FILE = 'TRAFFIC', STATUS = 'OLD')
      READ (2, *) ((FLOW(I, J), J = 2, 13), I = 1, 64)
*
*        Information in each three column group in the array is
*        stored in the following order:
*                Southbound
*                Westbound
*                Northbound
*                Eastbound
*
*        Within each group the data is stored in the
*        following order (by columns):
*                Right turning traffic
*                Through
*                Left turning
*
*        Add beginning time (in decimal hours) to
*        the first column of the array
*
      TIME = 6.0
      DO 50 I = 1, 64
         FLOW(I, 1) = TIME
         TIME = TIME + 0.25
   50 CONTINUE
*
*        Print header for hourly traffic flow numbers.
*
      PRINT 70
   70 FORMAT (/1X, 12X, 'AVERAGE TRAFFIC FLOW THROUGH ALBUQUERQUE',
     &         ' INTERSECTIONS', //1x, 8x, 'Time', 3x, 'Northbound',
     &         4x, 'Eastbound', 3x, 'Southbound', 3x, 'Westbound',
     &         3x, 'Total')
*
*        Count and print out hourly flows.
*
      TIME = 6.00
      DO 200 I = 1, 64, 4
*
*                Zero out hourly counters.
*
         HTOTAL = 0.0
```

```
            DO 110 J = 1, 4
                CNT(J) = 0.0
    110     CONTINUE
*
*               Sum up counters by direction, by quarter
*               hour data, and by all three flow patterns.
*
            DO 140 J = 1, 4
                DO 130 K = 0, 3
                    DO 120 L = 1, 3
                        CNT(J) = CNT(J) +
    &                           FLOW((I+K), ((J-1)*3 + 1 + L))
    120         CONTINUE
    130         CONTINUE
                HTOTAL = HTOTAL + CNT(J)
                AVG(J) = AVG(J) + CNT(J)
    140     CONTINUE
*
*               Print out hourly values.
*
            PRINT 150, INT(TIME), INT(CNT(3)), INT(CNT(4)),
    &                  INT(CNT(1)), INT(CNT(2)), INT(HTOTAL)
    150     FORMAT (1X, 7X, I2, ':00', 6X, I4, 10X, I4, 8X,
    &                   I4, 8X, I4, 6X, I4)
*
            TIME = TIME + 1.0
    200 CONTINUE
*
*       Calculate and print out the hourly averages for each direction
*       (use htotal to hold the sum of the hourly averages in all
*       directions).
*
        HTOTAL = 0.0
        DO 210 J = 1, 4
            AVG(J) = AVG(J) / 16.0
            HTOTAL = HTOTAL + AVG(J)
    210 CONTINUE
*
        PRINT 220, INT(AVG(3)), INT(AVG(4)), INT(AVG(1)),
    &              INT(AVG(2)), INT(HTOTAL)
    220 FORMAT (/1X, 6X, 'Average', 5X, I4, 10X, I4, 8X, I4,
    &              8X, I4, 6X, I4)
*
*       Find largest number of left hand turns
*       in a quarter hour period.
*
        LMAX = 0.0
        DO 300 I = 1, 64
            LTRNS = 0.0
            DO 250 J = 4, 13, 3
                LTRNS = LTRNS + FLOW(I,Jj)
    250     CONTINUE
            IF (LTRNS .GT. LMAX) LMAX = LTRNS
    300 CONTINUE
*
```

```fortran
*         Print out maximum number of left hand turns.
*
      PRINT 310, INT(LMAX)
  310 FORMAT (/1X, 7X, 'Maximum number of left hand ',
     &         'turns in a 15 minute period was ', I4)
*
*         Find consective one hour period with the
*         maximum traffic flow.
*
*         Set initital conditions.
*
      HMAX = 0.0
      HTIME = -1
      DO 330 J = 2, 13
         FQTR = FQTR + FLOW (1, J)
         SQTR = SQTR + FLOW (2, J)
         TQTR = TQTR + FLOW (3, J)
  330 CONTINUE
*
      DO 400 I = 1, 61
         LQTR = 0.0
         DO 350 J = 2, 13
            LQTR = LQTR + FLOW ((I + 3), J)
  350    CONTINUE
         HTOTAL = FQTR + SQTR + TQTR + LQTR
         IF (HTOTAL .GT. HMAX) THEN
            HMAX = HTOTAL
            HTIME = I
         ENDIF
*
*             Shift quarters for next hourly summation.
*
         FQTR = SQTR
         SQTR = TQTR
         TQTR = LQTR
  400 CONTINUE
*
      PRINT 410, FLOW(HTIME, 1)
  410 FORMAT (/1X, 10X, 'Maximum total flow for a one hour ',
     &         'period began at ', F5.2, ' hrs')
*
*         Find the maximum flow rate during a quarter
*         hour period for north-south or east-west
*         orientation.
*
      MAXNS = 0.0
      MAXEW = 0.0
      DO 500 I = 1, 64
         SUMNS = 0.0
         SUMEW = 0.0
         DO 450 L = 2, 8, 6
            DO 430 J = 1, 1+2
               SUMNS = SUMNS + FLOW(I,J)
               SUMEW = SUMEW + FLOW(I, J+3)
  430       CONTINUE
```

```
  450     CONTINUE
          IF (SUMNS .GT. MAXNS) MAXNS = SUMNS
          IF (SUMEW .GT. MAXEW) MAXEW = SUMEW
  500 CONTINUE
*
*       Print out results.
*
      IF (MAXNS .GT. MAXEW) THEN
         PRINT 520, INT(MAXNS)
  520    FORMAT (/1X, 20X, 'The maximum orientated flow',
     &               ' was ', I4, ' and', /1X, 22X, 'occured',
     &               ' in the north-south directions')
       ELSE
         PRINT 540, INT(MAXEW)
  540    FORMAT (/1X, 20X, 'The maximum orientated flow',
     &               ' was ', I4, ' and', /1X, 23X, 'occured',
     &               ' in the east-west directions')
       ENDIF
*
      END
*-------------------------------------------------------------*
```

CHAPTER 6 - SOLUTIONS TO TEXT PROBLEMS

Many of the solutions to text problems are included at the
end of the text.   This chapter contains solutions to all the
remaining problems so that a complete set of solutions is
available.   Answers which contain FORTRAN statements are not
always unique.   Therefore, while these answers represent good
solutions to the problems, they are not necessarily the only
valid solutions.

Chapter 2

1.
```
      *-----------------------------------------------------------*
            PROGRAM  CONVRT
      *
      *  This program converts dollars to francs.
      *
            REAL  FRANCS, DOLLAR
      *
            PRINT*, 'ENTER AMOUNT IN DOLLARS'
            READ*, DOLLAR
            FRANCS = DOLLAR*6.2
            PRINT 5, DOLLAR, FRANCS
          5 FORMAT (1X,F7.2,' DOLLARS = ',F7.2,' FRANCS ')
            END
      *-----------------------------------------------------------*
```

2.
```
      *-----------------------------------------------------------*
            PROGRAM  CONVRT
      *
      *  This program converts pounds sterling to dollars.
      *
            REAL  POUNDS, DOLLAR
      *
            PRINT*, 'ENTER AMOUNT IN POUNDS STERLING'
            READ*, POUNDS
            DOLLAR = POUNDS*1.95
            PRINT 5, POUNDS, DOLLAR
          5 FORMAT (1X,F7.2,' POUNDS STERLING = ',F7.2,
           +        ' DOLLARS')
            END
      *-----------------------------------------------------------*
```

3.
```
      *-----------------------------------------------------------*
            PROGRAM  CONVRT
      *
      *  This program converts deutsche marks to dollars.
      *
            REAL  DMARKS, DOLLAR
      *
            PRINT*, 'ENTER AMOUNT IN DEUTSCHE MARKS'
            READ*, DMARKS
            DOLLAR = DMARKS/2.4
            PRINT 5, DMARKS, DOLLAR
```

91

```
      5 FORMAT (1X,F7.2,' DEUTSCHE MARKS = ',F7.2,' DOLLARS ')
        END
*------------------------------------------------------------*
```

4.
```
*------------------------------------------------------------*
        PROGRAM  CONVRT
*
*   This program converts dollars to
*   pounds sterling and deutsche marks.
*
        REAL  DOLLAR, POUNDS, DMARKS
*
        PRINT*, 'ENTER AMOUNT IN DOLLARS'
        READ*, DOLLAR
        POUNDS = DOLLAR/1.95
        DMARKS = DOLLAR*2.4
        PRINT 5, DOLLAR
      5 FORMAT (1X,'DOLLARS = ',F7.2)
        PRINT 6, POUNDS
      6 FORMAT (1X,'POUNDS STERLING = ',F7.2)
        PRINT 7, DMARKS
      7 FORMAT (1X,'DEUTSCHE MARKS = ',F7.2)
        END
*------------------------------------------------------------*
```

5. Solution in text.

6.
```
*------------------------------------------------------------*
        PROGRAM  GROWTH
*
*   This program predicts bacteria growth.
*
        REAL  YOLD, YNEW, TIME
*
        PRINT*, 'ENTER INTIAL POPULATION'
        READ*, YOLD
        PRINT*, 'ENTER TIME ELAPSED IN MINUTES'
        READ*, TIME
        YNEW = YOLD*EXP(1.386*TIME/60.0)
        PRINT 10, YOLD
     10 FORMAT (1X,'INITIAL POPULATION = ',F9.4)
        PRINT 20, TIME
     20 FORMAT (1X,'TIME ELAPSED (MINUTES) = ',F9.4)
        PRINT 30, YNEW
     30 FORMAT (1X,'PREDICTED POPULATION = ',F9.4)
        END
*------------------------------------------------------------*
```

7.
```
*------------------------------------------------------------*
        PROGRAM  GROWTH
*
*   This program predicts bacteria growth.
*
        REAL  YOLD, YNEW, TIME
*
```

```
          PRINT*, 'ENTER INTIAL POPULATION'
          READ*, YOLD
          PRINT*, 'ENTER TIME ELAPSED IN DAYS'
          READ*, TIME
          YNEW = YOLD*EXP(1.386*TIME*24.0)
          PRINT 10, YOLD
       10 FORMAT (1X,'INITIAL POPULATION = ',F9.4)
          PRINT 20, TIME
       20 FORMAT (1X,'TIME ELAPSED (DAYS) = ',F9.4)
          PRINT 30, YNEW
       30 FORMAT (1X,'PREDICTED POPULATION = ',F9.4)
          END
     *------------------------------------------------------------*


8.   *------------------------------------------------------------*
          PROGRAM  GROWTH
     *
     *  This program predicts bacteria growth.
     *
          REAL  YOLD, Y2, Y3, PERC
     *
          PRINT*, 'ENTER INTIAL POPULATION'
          READ*, YOLD
          Y2 = YOLD*EXP(1.386*2.0)
          Y3 = YOLD*EXP(1.386*3.0)
          PERC = (Y3-Y2)/Y2*100.0
          PRINT 10, PERC
       10 FORMAT (1X,'PERCENT INCREASE FROM 2 TO 3 HOURS IS ',
         +          F6.2)
          END
     *------------------------------------------------------------*


9.   Solution in text.

10.  *------------------------------------------------------------*
          PROGRAM  GROWTH
     *
     *  This program predicts bacteria growth.
     *
          REAL  TIME1, TIME2, POP1, POP2, CHANGE
     *
          PRINT*, 'ENTER TIME1 (HOURS)'
          READ*, TIME1
          PRINT*, 'ENTER TIME2 (HOURS)'
          READ*, TIME2
          POP1 = EXP(1.386*TIME1)
          POP2 = EXP(1.386*TIME2)
          CHANGE = ABS(POP2 - POP1)
          PRINT 5, CHANGE
        5 FORMAT (1X,'AMOUNT OF GROWTH = ',F8.2)
          END
     *------------------------------------------------------------*


11.  *------------------------------------------------------------*
          PROGRAM  DATE
```

```
*
*    This program estimates the age of an artifact from
*    the proportion of carbon remaining in the artifact.
*
      INTEGER  AGE
      REAL   CARBON
*
      PRINT*, 'ENTER PROPORTION REMAINING FOR CARBON DATING'
      READ*, CARBON
      AGE = INT((-LOG(CARBON))/0.0001216)
      PRINT 5, AGE
    5 FORMAT (1X,'ESTIMATED AGE OF ARTIFACT IS ',I6,
     +          ' YEARS')
      END
*------------------------------------------------------------*
```

12.
```
*------------------------------------------------------------*
      PROGRAM  DATE
*
*    This program estimates the age of an artifact from
*    the proportion of carbon remaining in the artifact.
*
      INTEGER  AGE
      REAL   CARBON
*
      PRINT*, 'ENTER PROPORTION REMAINING FOR CARBON DATING'
      READ*, CARBON
      AGE = NINT((-LOG(CARBON))/0.0001216)
      PRINT 5, AGE
    5 FORMAT (1X,'ESTIMATED AGE OF ARTIFACT IS ',I6,
     +          ' YEARS')
      END
*------------------------------------------------------------*
```

13. Solution in text.

14.
```
*------------------------------------------------------------*
      PROGRAM  DATE
*
*    This program estimates the age of an artifact from
*    the propotion of carbon remaining in the artifact.
*
      INTEGER  CENTRY
      REAL   CARBON, AGE
*
      PRINT*, 'ENTER PROPORTION REMAINING FOR CARBON DATING'
      READ*, CARBON
      AGE = (-LOG(CARBON))/0.0001216
      CENTRY = INT(AGE/100.0)
      PRINT 5, CENTRY
    5 FORMAT (1X,'ESTIMATED AGE OF ARTIFACT IS ',I6,
     +          ' CENTURIES')
      END
*------------------------------------------------------------*
```

15. *--*
          PROGRAM DATE
    *
    * This program estimates the age of an artifact from
    * the propotion of carbon remaining in the artifact.
    *
          INTEGER CENTRY
          REAL CARBON, AGE
    *
          PRINT*, 'ENTER PROPORTION REMAINING FOR CARBON DATING'
          READ*, CARBON
          AGE = (-LOG(CARBON))/0.0001216
          CENTRY = NINT(AGE/100.0)
          PRINT 5, CENTRY
        5 FORMAT (1X,'ESTIMATED AGE OF ARTIFACT IS ',I6,
          +   ' CENTURIES')
          END
    --

16. *--*
          PROGRAM TRAIN
    *
    * This program computes the horizontal force
    * generated by a train on a level curve.
    *
          REAL WEIGHT, MPH, RADIUS, FORCE
    *
          PRINT*, 'ENTER WEIGHT OF TRAIN IN POUNDS'
          READ*, WEIGHT
          PRINT*, 'ENTER SPEED OF TRAIN IN MILES PER HOUR'
          READ*, MPH
          PRINT*, 'ENTER RADIUS OF CURVE IN FEET'
          READ*, RADIUS
    *
          FORCE = (WEIGHT/32.0)*
          +   ((MPH*1.4667)**2/RADIUS)
    *
          PRINT 10, WEIGHT
       10 FORMAT (1X,'TRAIN WEIGHT - ',F8.2,' POUNDS')
          PRINT 20, MPH
       20 FORMAT (1X,'TRAIN SPEED - ',F8.2,' MPH')
          PRINT 30, RADIUS
       30 FORMAT (1X,'CURVE RADIUS - ',F8.2,' FEET')
          PRINT*
          PRINT 40, FORCE
       40 FORMAT (1X,'RESULTING HORIZONTAL FORCE - ',
          +   F8.2,' POUNDS')
          END
    --

17. *--*
          PROGRAM TRAIN
    *
    * This program computes the horizontal force
    * generated by a train on a level curve.

                              95

```
*
       REAL  WEIGHT, MPH, RADIUS, FORCE
*
       PRINT*, 'ENTER WEIGHT OF TRAIN IN TONS'
       READ*, WEIGHT
       PRINT*, 'ENTER SPEED OF TRAIN IN MILES PER HOUR'
       READ*, MPH
       PRINT*, 'ENTER RADIUS OF CURVE IN YARDS'
       READ*, RADIUS
*
       FORCE  = (WEIGHT*2000.0/32.0)*
      +         ((MPH*1.4667)**2/(RADIUS*3.0))
*
       PRINT 10, WEIGHT
   10 FORMAT (1X,'TRAIN WEIGHT - ',F8.2,' TONS')
       PRINT 20, MPH
   20 FORMAT (1X,'TRAIN SPEED - ',F8.2,' MPH')
       PRINT 30, RADIUS
   30 FORMAT (1X,'CURVE RADIUS - ',F8.2,' YARDS')
       PRINT*
       PRINT 40, FORCE
   40 FORMAT (1X,'RESULTING HORIZONTAL FORCE - ',
      +         F8.2,' POUNDS')
       END
*------------------------------------------------------------*

18.  *------------------------------------------------------------*
       PROGRAM  TRAIN
*
*  This program computes the horizontal force
*  generated by a train on a level curve.
*
       INTEGER  FORCE
       REAL  WEIGHT, MPH, RADIUS
*
       PRINT*, 'ENTER WEIGHT OF TRAIN IN TONS'
       READ*, WEIGHT
       PRINT*, 'ENTER SPEED OF TRAIN IN MILES PER HOUR'
       READ*, MPH
       PRINT*, 'ENTER RADIUS OF CURVE IN FEET'
       READ*, RADIUS
*
       FORCE = INT((WEIGHT*2000.0/32.0)*
      +         ((MPH*1.4667)**2/RADIUS))
*
       PRINT 10, WEIGHT
   10 FORMAT (1X,'TRAIN WEIGHT - ',F8.2,' TONS')
       PRINT 20, MPH
   20 FORMAT (1X,'TRAIN SPEED - ',F8.2,' MPH')
       PRINT 30, RADIUS
   30 FORMAT (1X,'CURVE RADIUS - ',F8.2,' FEET')
       PRINT*
       PRINT 40, FORCE
   40 FORMAT (1X,'RESULTING HORIZONTAL FORCE - ',
      +         I8,' POUNDS')
```

96

```
          END
     *------------------------------------------------------------*

19.  Solution in text.

20.  *------------------------------------------------------------*
          PROGRAM  TRAIN
     *
     *   This program computes the horizontal force
     *   generated by a train on a level curve.
     *
          REAL  WEIGHT, MPH, RADIUS, KPH, FORCE
     *
          PRINT*, 'ENTER WEIGHT OF TRAIN IN TONS'
          READ*, WEIGHT
          PRINT*, 'ENTER SPEED OF TRAIN IN KILOMETERS PER HOUR'
          READ*, KPH
          PRINT*, 'ENTER RADIUS OF CURVE IN FEET'
          READ*, RADIUS
     *
          MPH = KPH/1.609
          FORCE = (WEIGHT*2000.0/32.0)*
         +         ((MPH*1.4667)**2/RADIUS)
     *
          PRINT 10, WEIGHT
       10 FORMAT (1X,'TRAIN WEIGHT - ',F8.2,' TONS')
          PRINT 20, KPH
       20 FORMAT (1X,'TRAIN SPEED - ',F8.2,' KPH')
          PRINT 30, RADIUS
       30 FORMAT (1X,'CURVE RADIUS - ',F8.2,' FEET')
          PRINT*
          PRINT 40, FORCE
       40 FORMAT (1X,'RESULTING HORIZONTAL FORCE - ',
         +         F8.2,' POUNDS')
          END
     *------------------------------------------------------------*

21.  *------------------------------------------------------------*
          PROGRAM  PAYROLL
     *
     *   This program computes a student salary.
     *
          REAL  HRS, RATE, PAY
     *
          PRINT*, 'ENTER HOURS WORKED AND HOURLY PAYRATE'
          READ*, HRS, RATE
          PAY = HRS*RATE
          PRINT 5, PAY
        5 FORMAT (1X,'STUDENT SALARY = $',F6.2)
          END
     *------------------------------------------------------------*

22.  *------------------------------------------------------------*
          PROGRAM  RECT
     *
```

```
      *   This program computes the perimeter and area
      *   of a rectangle
      *
          REAL  LENGTH, WIDTH, PERI, AREA
      *
          PRINT*, 'ENTER RECTANGLE LENGTH AND WIDTH'
          READ*, LENGTH, WIDTH
          PERI = 2.0*LENGTH + 2.0*WIDTH
          AREA = LENGTH*WIDTH
          PRINT 5, PERI
        5 FORMAT (1X,'PERIMETER = ',F9.2)
          PRINT 10, AREA
       10 FORMAT (1X,'AREA = ',F9.4)
          END
      *-------------------------------------------------------------*

23.   *-------------------------------------------------------------*
          PROGRAM  LINEAR
      *
      *   This program computes the slope
      *   of the line between two points.
      *
          REAL  X1, Y1, X2, Y2, SLOPE
      *
          PRINT*, 'ENTER X, Y FOR POINT 1'
          READ*, X1, Y1
          PRINT*, 'ENTER X, Y, FOR POINT 2'
          READ*, X2, Y2
          SLOPE = (Y2-Y1)/(X2-X1)
          PRINT 5, X1, Y1
        5 FORMAT (1X,' POINT 1 = ',F5.2,',',F5.2)
          PRINT 10, X2, Y2
       10 FORMAT (1X,'POINT 2 = ',F5.2,',',F5.2)
          PRINT 15, SLOPE
       15 FORMAT (1X,'SLOPE = ',F5.2)
          END
      *-------------------------------------------------------------*

24.   *-------------------------------------------------------------*
          PROGRAM CIRCLE
      *
      *   This program reads the diameter of a circle and computes
      *   the corresponding radius, circumference, and area.
      *
          REAL  PI, RADIUS, CIRCUM, AREA, DIAMTR
      *
          PRINT*, 'ENTER DIAMTER'
          READ*, DIAMTR
      *
          PI = 3.141593
          RADIUS = DIAMTR/2.0
          CIRCUM = PI*DIAMTR
          AREA = PI*RADIUS**2
          PRINT 5, DIAMTR
        5 FORMAT (1X,'PROPERTIES OF A CIRCLE WITH DIAMETER ',
```

```
           +        F8.3)
             PRINT 6, RADIUS
           6 FORMAT (1X,'(1)  RADIUS = ',F8.3)
             PRINT 7, CIRCUM
           7 FORMAT (1X,'(2)  CIRCUMFERENCE = ',F8.3)
             PRINT 8, AREA
           8 FORMAT (1X,'(3)  AREA = ',F8.3)
             END
    *------------------------------------------------------------*

25.  Solution in text.

26.  *------------------------------------------------------------*
             PROGRAM ANIMAL
      *
      *  This program prints a report on an experiment involving
      *  three test animals' weights.
      *
             INTEGER  NUM1, NUM2, NUM3
             REAL  BEGWT1, BEGWT2, BEGWT3,
           +       FNLWT1, FNLWT2, FNLWT3, PER1, PER2, PER3
      *
             PRINT*, 'ENTER ID#, BEGINNING WEIGHT, AND FINAL WEIGHT'
             READ*, NUM1, BEGWT1, FNLWT1
             READ*, NUM2, BEGWT2, FNLWT2
             READ*, NUM3, BEGWT3, FNLWT3
      *
             PER1 = (FNLWT1 - BEGWT1)/BEGWT1*100.0
             PER2 = (FNLWT2 - BEGWT2)/BEGWT2*100.0
             PER3 = (FNLWT3 - BEGWT3)/BEGWT3*100.0
      *
             PRINT*, '               TEST RESULTS'
             PRINT*, ' ID#  INITIAL WT  FINAL WT  PERCENT INCREASE'
             PRINT 5, NUM1, BEGWT1, FNLWT1, PER1
           5 FORMAT (1X,I3,5X,F5.3,5X,F5.3,5X,F6.2)
             PRINT 5, NUM2, BEGWT2, FNLWT2, PER2
             PRINT 5, NUM3, BEGWT3, FNLWT3, PER3
             END
    *------------------------------------------------------------*

27.  *------------------------------------------------------------*
             PROGRAM  COMB
      *
      *  This program computes the combined resistance
      *  for three resistors in parallel.
      *
             REAL  R1, R2, R3, RC
      *
             PRINT*, 'ENTER 3 RESISTANCES'
             READ*, R1, R2, R3
             RC = 1.0/(1.0/R1 + 1.0/R2 + 1.0/R3)
             PRINT 5, R1, R2, R3
           5 FORMAT (1X,'RESISTANCES:',F8.2,1X,F8.2,1X,F8.2)
             PRINT 10, RC
          10 FORMAT (1X,'PARALLEL COMBINATION:',F8.2)
```

```
          END
     *-------------------------------------------------------------*

28.  *-------------------------------------------------------------*
          PROGRAM DIST
     *
     *  This program calculates the distances
     *  between three sets of points.
     *
          REAL  X1, X2, X3, Y1, Y2, Y3, DIST12, DIST13, DIST23
     *
          PRINT*, 'ENTER X, Y FOR POINT #1'
          READ*, X1, Y1
          PRINT*, 'ENTER X, Y FOR POINT #2'
          READ*, X2, Y2
          PRINT*, 'ENTER X, Y FOR POINT #3'
          READ*, X3, Y3
     *
          DIST12 = SQRT((X1-X2)**2 + (Y1-Y2)**2)
          DIST13 = SQRT((X1-X3)**2 + (Y1-Y3)**2)
          DIST23 = SQRT((X2-X3)**2 + (Y2-Y3)**2)
     *
          PRINT*, 'DISTANCE BETWEEN POINTS 1 AND 2 IS:'
          PRINT 5, DIST12
        5 FORMAT (1X,F8.2)
          PRINT*, 'DISTANCE BETWEEN POINTS 1 AND 3 IS:'
          PRINT 5, DIST13
          PRINT*, 'DISTANC3 BETWEEN POINTS 2 AND 3 IS:'
          PRINT 5, DIST23
          END
     *-------------------------------------------------------------*

29.  *-------------------------------------------------------------*
          PROGRAM LABOR
     *
     *  This program computes the percentage of the labor force
     *  that is civilian and the percentage that is military.
     *
          INTEGER  YEAR
          REAL  NUMCIV, NUMMIL, THOCIV, THOMIL, TOTAL,
         +      PERCIV, PERMIL, THOTOT, PERTOT
     *
          PRINT*, 'ENTER YEAR, # OF CIVILIANS,'
         +        ' # OF PEOPLE IN MILITARY'
          READ*, YEAR, NUMCIV, NUMMIL
     *
          THOCIV = NUMCIV/1000.0
          THOMIL = NUMMIL/1000.0
          TOTAL = NUMCIV + NUMMIL
          PERCIV = NUMCIV/TOTAL*100.0
          PERMIL = NUMMIL/TOTAL*100.0
          THOTOT = THOCIV + THOMIL
          PERTOT = PERCIV + PERMIL
     *
          PRINT 5, YEAR
```

```
   5 FORMAT (1X,'LABOR FORCE - YEAR ',I4)
     PRINT*, 'NUMBER OF WORKERS (THOUSANDS)',
    +        ' AND PERCENTAGE OF WORKERS'
     PRINT 6, THOCIV, PERCIV
   6 FORMAT (1X,'CIVILIAN',8X,F7.3,13X,F7.3)
     PRINT 7, THOMIL, PERMIL
   7 FORMAT (1X,'MILITARY',8X,F7.3,13X,F7.3)
     PRINT 8, THOTOT, PERTOT
   8 FORMAT (1X,'TOTAL',11X,F7.3,13X,F7.3)
     END
*-------------------------------------------------------*
```

30.
```
*-------------------------------------------------------*
     PROGRAM  TRAVEL
*
* This program calculates the time required for electrons to
* travel from the cathode to the anode of a rectifier tube.
*
     REAL  Q, M, V, R1, R2, Z, TIME
*
     Q = 1.60206E-19
     M = 9.1083E-31
*
     PRINT*, 'ENTER VOLTAGE, INNER RADIUS, OUTER RADIUS'
     READ*, V, R1, R2
*
     Z = R2/R1
     TIME = SQRT(2.0*M/Q/V)*R1*Z*(1.0+Z/3.0+Z**2/10.0+
    +       Z**3/42.0+Z**4/216.0)
*
     PRINT*
     PRINT 5, V
   5 FORMAT (1X,'ACCELERATING VOLTAGE =',E12.5)
     PRINT 6, R1
   6 FORMAT (1X,'INNER RADIUS          =',E12.5)
     PRINT 7, R2
   7 FORMAT (1X,'OUTER RADIUS          =',E12.5)
     PRINT 8, SECS
   8 FORMAT (1X,'TIME FOR ELECTRONS TO TRAVEL IS',
    +       E12.5,' SECS')
     END
*-------------------------------------------------------*
```

31.
```
*-------------------------------------------------------*
     PROGRAM VOLUME
*
* This program calculates the volume of a hollow sphere.
*
     REAL  VOLUME, VOL1, VOL2, RADUS1, RADUS2, THICK
*
     PRINT*, 'ENTER THE OUTER RADIUS AND THICKNESS OF SPHERE'
     READ*, RADUS1, THICK
*
     RADUS2 = RADUS1 - THICK
     VOL1 = 4.0/3.0*3.141593*RADUS1**3
```

```
          VOL2 = 4.0/3.0*3.141593*RADUS2**3
          VOLUME = ABS(VOL1 - VOL2)
   *
          PRINT*
          PRINT 5, VOLUME
        5 FORMAT (1X,'VOLUME OF THE SHELL OF THE SPHERE IS ',
       +          E12.5)
          END
   *------------------------------------------------------------*
```

32.
```
   *------------------------------------------------------------*
          PROGRAM GAUSS
   *
   *  This program calculates and prints a Gaussian function.
   *
          REAL  X, Y
   *
          PRINT*, 'ENTER X'
          READ*, X
   *
          Y = 1.0/SQRT(2.0*3.141593)*EXP(-0.5*X**2)
   *
          PRINT *,'THE STANDARD NORMAL DENSITY FUNCTION'
          PRINT 5, X, Y
        5 FORMAT (1X,'AT ',F6.2,' GIVES A VALUE OF ',F8.5)
          END
   *------------------------------------------------------------*
```

33.
```
   *------------------------------------------------------------*
          PROGRAM GAUSS
   *
   *  This program computes the difference between different
   *  sets of data.
   *
          REAL  Y0, Y1 ,Y2, Y3, DIF01, DIF12, DIF23
   *
          Y0 = 1.0/SQRT(2.0*3.141593)*EXP(-0.5*0.0**2)
          Y1 = 1.0/SQRT(2.0*3.141593)*EXP(-0.5*1.0**2)
          Y2 = 1.0/SQRT(2.0*3.141593)*EXP(-0.5*2.0**2)
          Y3 = 1.0/SQRT(2.0*3.141593)*EXP(-0.5*3.0**2)
          DIF01 = Y1 - Y0
          DIF12 = Y2 - Y1
          DIF23 = Y3 - Y2
   *
          PRINT 5
        5 FORMAT (1X,3X,'STANDARD GAUSSIAN DENSITY FUNCTION')
          PRINT*
          PRINT 6, DIF01
        6 FORMAT (1X,'X: 0.0 TO 1.0',7X,'CHANGE IN Y:  ',F6.2)
          PRINT 7, DIF02
        7 FORMAT (1X,'X: 1.0 TO 2.0',7X,'CHANGE IN Y:  ',F6.2)
          PRINT 8, DIF03
        8 FORMAT (1X,'X: 2.0 TO 3.0',7X,'CHANGE IN Y:  ',F6.2)
          END
   *------------------------------------------------------------*
```

```
34.  *-------------------------------------------------------------*
          PROGRAM AREA
      *
      * This program calculates the area of a triangle using the
      * three inputed vertices.
      *
          REAL  X1, X2, X3, Y1, Y2, Y3, AREA
      *
          PRINT*, 'ENTER THREE LINES OF X AND Y COORDINATES'
          READ*, X1, Y1
          READ*, X2, Y2
          READ*, X3, Y3
      *
          AREA = 0.5*ABS(X1*Y2 - X2*Y1 + X2*Y3 - X3*Y2 + X3*Y1
         +                + X1*Y3)
      *
          PRINT*, 'TRIANGLE VERTICES:'
          PRINT 5, X1
        5 FORMAT (1X,'(1) ',F5.1)
          PRINT 6, X2
        6 FORMAT (1X,'(2) ',F5.1)
          PRINT 7, X3
        7 FORMAT (1X,'(3) ',F5.1)
          PRINT*
          PRINT*, 'TRIANGLE AREA:'
          PRINT 8, AREA
        8 FORMAT (1X,5X,F6.2)
          END
     *-------------------------------------------------------------*


35.  *-------------------------------------------------------------*
          PROGRAM DECAY
      *
      * This program calculates radioactive decay of thorium.
      *
          REAL  NBEG, NFINAL, TIME
      *
          PRINT*, 'ENTER AMOUNT OF THORIUM AND TIME TO ELASPE'
          READ*, NBEG, TIME
      *
          NFINAL = NBEG*EXP(-0.693*TIME/1.65E+16)
      *
          PRINT 5, NBEG
        5 FORMAT (1X,'INITIAL VALUE OF THORIUM:  ',F7.3)
          PRINT 6, TIME
        6 FORMAT (1X,'TIME ELAPSED:              ',F7.3)
          PRINT 7, NFINAL
        7 FORMAT (1X,'REMAINING THORIUM:         ',F7.3)
          END
     *-------------------------------------------------------------*
```

CHAPTER 3

1.
```
*---------------------------------------------------------*
      PROGRAM  ROCKET
*
* This program simulates a rocket flight.
*
      REAL  TIME, HEIGHT
*
      TIME = 0.0
      HEIGHT = 60.0
      PRINT 5
    5 FORMAT (1X,'TIME (SEC.)     HEIGHT (FT.)')
      PRINT*
*
   10 IF (HEIGHT.GT.0.0.AND.TIME.LE.50.0) THEN
         HEIGHT = 60.0 + 2.13*TIME**2 - 0.0013*TIME**4
     +              + 0.000034*TIME**4.751
         PRINT 15, TIME, HEIGHT
   15    FORMAT (1X,F7.4,8X,F9.4)
         IF(HEIGHT.LT.50.0) THEN
            TIME = TIME + 0.05
         ELSE
            TIME = TIME + 2.0
         ENDIF
         GO TO 10
      ENDIF
*
      END
*---------------------------------------------------------*
```

2.
```
*---------------------------------------------------------*
      PROGRAM  ROCKET
*
* This program simulates a rocket flight.
*
      REAL  TIME, HEIGHT
*
      TIME = 0.0
      HEIGHT = 60.0
      PRINT 5
    5 FORMAT (1X,'TIME (SEC.)     HEIGHT (FT.)')
      PRINT*
*
   10 IF (HEIGHT.GT.0.0.AND.TIME.LE.100.0) THEN
         HEIGHT = 60.0 + 2.13*TIME**2 - 0.0013*TIME**4
     +              + 0.000034*TIME**4.751
         PRINT 15, TIME, HEIGHT
   15    FORMAT (1X,F7.4,8X,F9.4)
         IF (HEIGHT.LT.50.0) THEN
            TIME = TIME + 0.25
         ELSE
            TIME = TIME + 1.0   )
         ENDIF
         GO TO 10
```

104

```
            ENDIF
     *
            END
     *------------------------------------------------------------*

3.   *------------------------------------------------------------*
            PROGRAM   ROCKET
     *
     *   This program simulates a rocket flight.
     *
            REAL   TIME, HEIGHT
     *
            TIME = 0.0
            HEIGHT = 60.0
            PRINT 5
          5 FORMAT (1X,'TIME (SEC.)     HEIGHT (FT.)')
            PRINT*
     *
         10 IF (HEIGHT.GT.0.0.AND.TIME.LE.100.0) THEN
                HEIGHT = 60.0 + 2.13*TIME**2 - 0.0013*TIME**4
          +            + 0.000034*TIME**4.751
                PRINT 15, TIME, HEIGHT
         15     FORMAT (1X,F7.4,8X,F9.4)
                IF (HEIGHT.LT.50.0) THEN
                    TIME = TIME + 0.25
                ELSE
                    TIME = TIME + 0.5
                ENDIF
                GO TO 10
            ENDIF
     *
            END
     *------------------------------------------------------------*

4.   *------------------------------------------------------------*
            PROGRAM   ROCKET
     *
     *   This program simulates a rocket flight.
     *
            REAL   TIME, HEIGHT, INCR1, INCR2
     *
            TIME = 0.0
            HEIGHT = 60.0
            PRINT*, 'ENTER TIME INCREMENT FOR DISTANCE'
            PRINT*, ' > OR = 50 FEET'
            READ*, INCR1
            PRINT*, 'ENTER TIME INCREMENT FOR DISTANCE'
            PRINT*, ' <  OR = 50 FEET'
            READ*, INCR2
            PRINT 5
          5 FORMAT (1X,'TIME (SEC.)     HEIGHT (FT.)')
            PRINT*
     *
         10 IF (HEIGHT.GT.0.0.AND.TIME.LE.100.0) THEN
                HEIGHT = 60.0 + 2.13*TIME**2 - 0.0013*TIME**4
```

105

```
     +                   + 0.000034*TIME**4.751
            PRINT 15, TIME, HEIGHT
      15    FORMAT (1X,F7.4,8X,F9.4)
            IF(HEIGHT.LT.50.0) THEN
               TIME = TIME + INCR2
            ELSE
               TIME = TIME + INCR1
            ENDIF
            GO TO 10
         ENDIF
*
         END
*-----------------------------------------------------------------*
```

5.   Solution in text.

6.
```
    *-----------------------------------------------------------------*
         PROGRAM   TIMBER
    *
    *  This program computes a reforestation summary
    *  for an area which has not been completely harvested.
    *
         INTEGER  ID, YEAR, N
         REAL  TOTAL, UNCUT, RATE, REFOR
    *
         PRINT*, 'ENTER LAND IDENTIFICATION (INTEGER)'
         READ*, ID
         PRINT*, 'ENTER TOTAL NUMBER OF ACRES'
         READ*, TOTAL
         PRINT*, 'ENTER NUMBER OF ACRES UNCUT'
         READ*, UNCUT
         PRINT*, 'ENTER REFORESTATION RATE'
         READ*, RATE
         PRINT*, 'ENTER NUMBER OF YEARS FOR TABLE'
         READ*, N
    *
         IF (UNCUT.GT.TOTAL) THEN
            PRINT*, 'UNCUT AREA LARGER THAN ENTIRE AREA'
         ELSE
            PRINT*
            PRINT*, 'REFORESTATION SUMMARY'
            PRINT*
            PRINT 5, ID
      5     FORMAT (1X,'IDENTIFICATION NUMBER ',I5)
            PRINT 10, TOTAL
      10    FORMAT (1X,'TOTAL ACRES = ',F10.2)
            PRINT 20, UNCUT
      20    FORMAT (1X,'UNCUT ACRES = ',F10.2)
            PRINT 30, RATE
      30    FORMAT (1X,'REFORESTATION RATE = ',F5.3)
            PRINT*
            PRINT*, 'YEAR  REFORESTED   TOTAL REFORESTED'
            DO 50 YEAR=1,N
               REFOR = UNCUT*RATE
               UNCUT = UNCUT + REFOR
```

```
              PRINT 40, YEAR, REFOR, UNCUT
40            FORMAT (1X,I3,F11.3,F17.3)
50     CONTINUE
       ENDIF
*
       END
*------------------------------------------------------------*


7.  Solution in text.

8.     *------------------------------------------------------------*
       PROGRAM  TIMBER
*
*  This program computes a reforestation summary
*  for an area which has not been completely harvested.
*
       INTEGER  ID, YEAR, M
       REAL  TOTAL, UNCUT, RATE, REFOR
*
       PRINT*, 'ENTER LAND IDENTIFICATION (INTEGER)'
       READ*, ID
       PRINT*, 'ENTER TOTAL NUMBER OF ACRES'
       READ*, TOTAL
       PRINT*, 'ENTER NUMBER OF ACRES UNCUT'
       READ*, UNCUT
       PRINT*, 'ENTER REFORESTATION RATE'
       READ*, RATE
       PRINT*, 'ENTER NUMBER OF YEARS BETWEEN LINES IN TABLE'
       READ*, M
*
       IF (UNCUT.GT.TOTAL) THEN
          PRINT*, 'UNCUT AREA LARGER THAN ENTIRE AREA'
       ELSE
          PRINT*
          PRINT*, 'REFORESTATION SUMMARY'
          PRINT*
          PRINT 5, ID
5         FORMAT (1X,'IDENTIFICATION NUMBER ',I5)
          PRINT 10, TOTAL
10        FORMAT (1X,'TOTAL ACRES = ',F10.2)
          PRINT 20, UNCUT
20        FORMAT (1X,'UNCUT ACRES = ',F10.2)
          PRINT 30, RATE
30        FORMAT (1X,'REFORESTATION RATE = ',F5.3)
          PRINT*
          PRINT*, 'YEAR  REFORESTED  TOTAL REFORESTED'
          DO 50 YEAR=1,20
             REFOR = UNCUT*RATE
             UNCUT = UNCUT + REFOR
             IF (MOD(YEAR,M).EQ.0) THEN
                PRINT 40, YEAR, REFOR, UNCUT
40              FORMAT (1X,I3,F11.3,F17.3)
             ENDIF
50        CONTINUE
```

107

```
        ENDIF
*
        END
*------------------------------------------------------------*


9.      *------------------------------------------------------------*
        PROGRAM  TIMBER
*
*  This program computes a reforestation summary
*  for an area which has not been completely harvested.
*
        INTEGER  ID, YEAR
        REAL  TOTAL, UNCUT, CUT, RATE, REFOR, TREFOR
*
        PRINT*, 'ENTER LAND IDENTIFICATION (INTEGER)'
        READ*, ID
        PRINT*, 'ENTER TOTAL NUMBER OF ACRES'
        READ*, TOTAL
        PRINT*, 'ENTER NUMBER OF ACRES UNCUT'
        READ*, UNCUT
        PRINT*, 'ENTER REFORESTATION RATE'
        READ*, RATE
*
        IF (UNCUT.GT.TOTAL) THEN
            PRINT*, 'UNCUT AREA LARGER THAN ENTIRE AREA'
        ELSE
            PRINT*
            PRINT*, 'REFORESTATION SUMMARY'
            PRINT*
            PRINT 5, ID
    5       FORMAT (1X,'IDENTIFICATION NUMBER ',I5)
            PRINT 10, TOTAL
   10       FORMAT (1X,'TOTAL ACRES = ',F10.2)
            PRINT 20, UNCUT
   20       FORMAT (1X,'UNCUT ACRES = ',F10.2)
            PRINT 30, RATE
   30       FORMAT (1X,'REFORESTATION RATE = ',F5.3)
            PRINT*
            PRINT*, 'YEAR  REFORESTED  TOTAL REFORESTED'
            CUT = TOTAL - UNCUT
            YEAR = 0
            REFOR = 0.0
            TREFOR = 0.0
   35       IF (TREFOR.LT.0.10*CUT) THEN
                YEAR = YEAR + 1
                REFOR = UNCUT*RATE
                UNCUT = UNCUT + REFOR
                TREFOR = TREFOR + REFOR
                PRINT 40, YEAR, REFOR, UNCUT
   40           FORMAT (1X,I3,F11.3,F17.3)
                GO TO 35
            ENDIF
        ENDIF
*
        END
```

108

```
    *------------------------------------------------------------*
10. *------------------------------------------------------------*
        PROGRAM  TIMBER
    *
    * This program computes a reforestation summary
    * for an area which has not been completely harvested.
    *
        INTEGER  ID, YEAR
        REAL  TOTAL, UNCUT, RATE, REFOR, UNCUT1
    *
        PRINT*, 'ENTER LAND IDENTIFICATION (INTEGER)'
        READ*, ID
        PRINT*, 'ENTER TOTAL NUMBER OF ACRES'
        READ*, TOTAL
        PRINT*, 'ENTER NUMBER OF ACRES UNCUT'
        READ*, UNCUT1
        PRINT*, 'ENTER REFORESTATION RATE'
        READ*, RATE
    *
        IF (UNCUT.GT.TOTAL) THEN
            PRINT*, 'UNCUT AREA LARGER THAN ENTIRE AREA'
        ELSE
            PRINT*
            PRINT*, 'REFORESTATION SUMMARY'
            PRINT*
            PRINT 5, ID
    5       FORMAT (1X,'IDENTIFICATION NUMBER ',I5)
            PRINT 10, TOTAL
    10      FORMAT (1X,'TOTAL ACRES = ',F10.2)
            PRINT 20, UNCUT1
    20      FORMAT (1X,'UNCUT ACRES = ',F10.2)
    25      IF (RATE.NE.0.0) THEN
                UNCUT = UNCUT1
                PRINT 30, RATE
    30          FORMAT (1X,'REFORESTATION RATE = ',F5.3)
                PRINT*
                PRINT*, 'YEAR  REFORESTED   TOTAL REFORESTED'
                DO 50 YEAR=1,20
                    REFOR = UNCUT*RATE
                    UNCUT = UNCUT + REFOR
                    IF (MOD(YEAR,20).EQ.0) THEN
                        PRINT 40, YEAR, REFOR, UNCUT
    40                  FORMAT (1X,I3,F11.3,F17.3)
                    ENDIF
    50          CONTINUE
                PRINT*, 'ENTER REFORESTATION RATE'
                READ*, RATE
                GO TO 25
            ENDIF
        ENDIF
    *
        END
    *------------------------------------------------------------*
```

```
11.  *---------------------------------------------------------------*
          PROGRAM  CABLE
     *
     *  This program computes the velocity of a cable car
     *  on a thousand-foot cable with three towers.
     *
          INTEGER TOTDIS, DIST, TOWER
          REAL  VEL
     *
          PRINT 1
        1 FORMAT (1X,9X,'CABLE CAR REPORT')
          PRINT*
          PRINT 2
        2 FORMAT (1X,'DISTANCE  NEAREST TOWER  VELOCITY')
          PRINT 3
        3 FORMAT (1X,'  (FT)',19X,'(FT/SEC)')
          PRINT*
     *
          TOTDIS = 0
        5 IF (TOTDIS.LE.1000) THEN
             IF (TOTDIS.LE.250) THEN
                TOWER = 1
                DIST = TOTDIS
             ELSEIF (TOTDIS.LE.750) THEN
                TOWER = 2
                DIST = ABS(TOTDIS - 500)
             ELSE
                TOWER = 3
                DIST = 1000 - TOTDIS
             ENDIF
             IF (DIST.LE.30) THEN
                VEL = 2.425 + 0.00175*DIST*DIST
             ELSE
                VEL = 0.625 + 0.12*DIST - 0.00025*DIST*DIST
             ENDIF
             PRINT 30, TOTDIS, TOWER, VEL
       30    FORMAT (1X,I4,11X,I1,9X,F7.2)
             TOTDIS = TOTDIS + 10
             GO TO 5
          ENDIF
     *
          END
     *---------------------------------------------------------------*


12.  *---------------------------------------------------------------*
          PROGRAM  CABLE
     *
     *  This program computes the velocity of a cable car
     *  on a thousand-foot cable with three towers.
     *
          INTEGER TOTDIS, DIST, TOWER, INCR
          REAL  VEL
     *
          PRINT*, 'ENTER DISTANCE INCREMENT FOR TABLE'
          READ*, INCR
```

```
      PRINT*
      PRINT 2
  2 FORMAT (1X,9X,'CABLE CAR REPORT')
      PRINT*
      PRINT 3
  3 FORMAT (1X,'DISTANCE  NEAREST TOWER   VELOCITY')
      PRINT 4
  4 FORMAT (1X,'  (FT)',19X,'(FT/SEC)')
      PRINT*
*
      DO 40 TOTDIS=0,1000,INCR
         IF (TOTDIS.LE.250) THEN
            TOWER = 1
            DIST = TOTDIS
         ELSEIF (TOTDIS.LE.750) THEN
            TOWER = 2
            DIST = ABS(TOTDIS - 500)
         ELSE
            TOWER = 3
            DIST = 1000 - TOTDIS
         ENDIF
         IF (DIST.LE.30) THEN
            VEL = 2.425 + 0.00175*DIST*DIST
         ELSE
            VEL = 0.625 + 0.12*DIST - 0.00025*DIST*DIST
         ENDIF
         PRINT 30, TOTDIS, TOWER, VEL
  30     FORMAT (1X,I4,11X,I1,9X,F7.2)
  40 CONTINUE
*
      END
*------------------------------------------------------------*


13. *------------------------------------------------------------*
         PROGRAM  CABLE
*
* This program computes the velocity of a cable car
* on a thousand-foot cable with three towers.
*
      INTEGER TOTDIS, DIST, TOWER
      REAL  VEL
*
      PRINT 1
  1 FORMAT (1X,9X,'CABLE CAR REPORT')
      PRINT*
      PRINT 2
  2 FORMAT (1X,'DISTANCE  NEAREST TOWER   VELOCITY',
      +          '   DISTANCE TO NEAREST TOWER')
      PRINT 3
  3 FORMAT (1X,'  (FT)',19X,'(FT/SEC)',15X,'(FT)')
      PRINT*
*
      DO 50 TOTDIS=0,1000,10
         IF (TOTDIS.LE.250) THEN
            TOWER = 1
```

```
              DIST = TOTDIS
          ELSEIF (TOTDIS.LE.750) THEN
              TOWER = 2
              DIST = ABS(TOTDIS - 500)
          ELSE
              TOWER = 3
              DIST = 1000 - TOTDIS
          ENDIF
          IF (DIST.LE.30) THEN
              VEL = 2.425 + 0.00175*DIST*DIST
          ELSE
              VEL = 0.625 + 0.12*DIST - 0.00025*DIST*DIST
          ENDIF
          PRINT 30, TOTDIS, TOWER, VEL, DIST
   30     FORMAT (1X,I4,11X,I1,9X,F7.2,15X,I4)
   50 CONTINUE
*
      END
*------------------------------------------------------------*

14.  *------------------------------------------------------------*
      PROGRAM  CABLE
*
*  This program computes the velocity of a cable car
*  on a thousand-foot cable with three towers.
*
      INTEGER TOTDIS, DIST, TOWER
      REAL   VEL
*
      PRINT 1
    1 FORMAT (1X,9X,'CABLE CAR REPORT')
      PRINT*
      PRINT 2
    2 FORMAT (1X,'DISTANCE  NEAREST TOWER  VELOCITY')
      PRINT 3
    3 FORMAT (1X,'  (FT)',19X,'(FT/SEC)')
      PRINT*
*
      TOTDIS = 0
    5 IF (TOTDIS.LE.1000) THEN
          IF (TOTDIS.LE.250) THEN
              TOWER = 1
              DIST = TOTDIS
          ELSEIF (TOTDIS.LE.750) THEN
              TOWER = 2
              DIST = ABS(TOTDIS - 500)
          ELSE
              TOWER = 3
              DIST = 1000 - TOTDIS
          ENDIF
          IF (DIST.LE.30) THEN
              VEL = 2.425 + 0.00175*DIST*DIST
          ELSE
              VEL = 0.625 + 0.12*DIST - 0.00025*DIST*DIST
          ENDIF
```

```
              PRINT 30, TOTDIS, TOWER, VEL, DIST
       30     FORMAT (1X,I4,11X,I1,9X,F7.2,15X,I4)
              IF (DIST.GE.20) THEN
                 TOTDIS = TOTDIS + 10
              ELSE
                 TOTDIS = TOTDIS + 5
              ENDIF
              GO TO 5
           ENDIF
   *
           END
   *------------------------------------------------------------*
```

15. Solution in text.

16.
```
   *------------------------------------------------------------*
           PROGRAM TABLE
   *
   *   This program prints a table of funtion values.
   *
           INTEGER  K, M
   *
           PRINT*, 'TABLE OF FUNCTION VALUES'
           PRINT*
           PRINT*, '        M             K'
           PRINT*
   *
           DO 10 M = 1,4
              K = 3*M
              PRINT 5, M, K
        5     FORMAT (1X,7X,I1,9X,I2)
       10 CONTINUE
   *
           END
   *------------------------------------------------------------*
```

17.
```
   *------------------------------------------------------------*
           PROGRAM  TABLE
   *
   *   This program prints a table of function values.
   *
           INTEGER  I, K
   *
           PRINT*, 'TABLE OF FUNCTION VALUES'
           PRINT*
           PRINT*, ' I         K'
           PRINT*
           DO 10 I=0,20
              K = I*I + 2*I + 2
              PRINT 5, I, K
        5     FORMAT (1X,I2,5X,I3)
       10 CONTINUE
   *
           END
   *------------------------------------------------------------*
```

18. *---*
```
      PROGRAM TABLE
*
*   This program prints a table of function values.
*
      INTEGER  I
      REAL  X, Y
*
      PRINT*, 'TABLE OF FUNCTION VALUES'
      PRINT*
      PRINT*, '        X           Y'
      PRINT*
*
      DO 10 I = 3,18
         X = REAL(I)*0.5
         Y = (X*X - 9.0)/(X*X + 2.0)
         PRINT 5, X, Y
    5    FORMAT (1X,6X,F3.1,6X,F7.4)
   10 CONTINUE
*
      END
```
     ---

19. Solution in text.

20. *---*
```
      PROGRAM TABLE
*
*   This program prints a table of consecutive even integers
*   and their squares.
*
      INTEGER  I
*
      PRINT*, 'TABLE OF INTEGERS AND SQUARES'
      PRINT*
      PRINT*, '       I      AND        I*I'
      PRINT*
*
      I = 2
    5 IF (I.LE.200) THEN
         PRINT 10, I, I*I
   10    FORMAT (1X,6X,I3,12X,I5)
         I = I + 2
         GO TO 5
      ENDIF
*
      END
```
     ---

21. *---*
```
      PROGRAM  TABLE
*
*   This program prints atable of function values.
*
```

114

```
        REAL  X, XSQ, FINAL
 *
        PRINT* 'ENTER A FINAL VALUE FOR X'
        READ*, X
        PRINT*, 'TABLE OF FUNCTION VALUES'
        PRINT*
        PRINT*, ' X         X SQUARED'
        PRINT*
      5 IF (X.LE.FINAL) THEN
            PRINT 10, X, X*X
     10     FORMAT (1X,F5.1,5X,F9.2)
            X = X + 0.5
            GO TO 5
        ENDIF
 *
        END
 *------------------------------------------------------------*
```

22.
```
 *------------------------------------------------------------*
        PROGRAM STUDENT
 *
 *  This program classifies students by
 *  number of hours completed.
 *
        INTEGER  NUMBER, HOURS
 *
        PRINT*, '                    REGISTRATION REPORT'
        PRINT*
        PRINT*, '            STUDENT ID AND CLASSIFICATION'
        PRINT*
 *
        READ (5,*) NUMBER, HOURS
      5 IF (NUMBER.NE.9999) THEN
            IF (HOURS.LT.30) THEN
                PRINT 10, NUMBER
     10         FORMAT (1X,11X,I6,9X,'FRESHMAN')
            ELSEIF (HOURS.LT.60) THEN
                PRINT 15, NUMBER
     15         FORMAT (1X,11X,I6,9X,'SOPHOMORE')
            ELSEIF (HOURS.LT.90) THEN
                PRINT 20, NUMBER
     20         FORMAT (1X,11X,I6,11X,'JUNIOR')
            ELSE
                PRINT 25, NUMBER
     25         FORMAT (1X,11X,I6,11X,'SENIOR')
            ENDIF
            READ (5,*) NUMBER, HOURS
            GO TO 5
        ENDIF
 *
        END
 *------------------------------------------------------------*
```

23.
```
 *------------------------------------------------------------*
        PROGRAM STUDENT
```

```
*
*   This program classifies students by
*   number of hours completed.
*
      INTEGER  NUMBER, HOURS, CNTFRE, CNTSOP, CNTJUN, CNTSEN
*
      CNTFRE = 0
      CNTSOP = 0
      CNTJUN = 0
      CNTSEN = 0
*
      PRINT*, '                REGISTRATION REPORT'
      PRINT*
      PRINT*, '            STUDENT ID AND CLASSIFICATION'
      PRINT*
*
      READ (5,*) NUMBER, HOURS
    5 IF (NUMBER.NE.9999) THEN
         IF (HOURS.LT.30) THEN
            CNTFRE = CNTFRE + 1
            PRINT 10, NUMBER
   10       FORMAT (1X,11X,I6,9X,'FRESHMAN')
         ELSEIF (HOURS.LT.60) THEN
            CNTSOP = CNTSOP + 1
            PRINT 15, NUMBER
   15       FORMAT (1X,11X,I6,9X,'SOPHOMORE')
         ELSEIF (HOURS.LT.90) THEN
            CNTJUN = CNTJUN + 1
            PRINT 20, NUMBER
   20       FORMAT (1X,11X,I6,11X,'JUNIOR')
         ELSE
            CNTSEN = CNTSEN + 1
            PRINT 25, NUMBER
   25       FORMAT (1X,11X,I6,11X,'SENIOR')
         ENDIF
         READ (5,*) NUMBER, HOURS
         GO TO 5
      ENDIF
*
      PRINT*
      PRINT*, 'REGISTRATION SUMMARY'
      PRINT*
      PRINT 30, CNTFRE
   30 FORMAT (' FRESHMEN       ',I5)
      PRINT 35, CNTSOP
   35 FORMAT (' SOPHOMORES     ',I5)
      PRINT 40, CNTJUN
   40 FORMAT (' JUNIORS        ',I5)
      PRINT 45, CNTSEN
   45 FORMAT (' SENIORS        ',I5)
      PRINT*
      PRINT 50, CNTFRE + CNTSOP + CNTJUN + CNTSEN
   50 FORMAT (' TOTAL STUDENTS        ',I6)
*
      END
```

```
      *-----------------------------------------------------------*
 24.  *-----------------------------------------------------------*
      PROGRAM ROCKET
      *
      *     This program simulates a rocket flight.
      *
            REAL   T, ACCELE, VELOCI, DISTAN
            INTEGER   TIME
      *
            PRINT*, '            ROCKET FLIGHT SIMULATION'
            PRINT*
            PRINT*, ' TIME     ACCELERATION     VELOCITY     DISTANCE'
            PRINT*, ' (SEC)    (FT/SEC*SEC)     (FT/SEC)       (FT)'
            PRINT*
      *
            DO 10 TIME = 0,50
               T = REAL(TIME)
               ACCELE = 4.25 - 0.015*T**2
               VELOCI = 4.25*T - 0.005*T**3
               DISTAN = 90 + 2.125*T**2 - 0.00125*T**4
               PRINT 5, T, ACCELE, VELOCI, DISTAN
         5     FORMAT (1X,2X,F6.2,5X,F7.2,7X,F7.2,5X,F8.2)
        10 CONTINUE
      *
            END
      *-----------------------------------------------------------*

 25.  *-----------------------------------------------------------*
      PROGRAM GERM
      *
      * This program computes germ growth.
      *
            REAL   CELLS, RATE, DISH, PERARE
            INTEGER   CULTUR, NUMBER, GENERA, ICELLS, DIAMTR
      *
            PRINT*, '                        OMEGA GERM GROWTH'
            PRINT*
      *
            DO 20 CULTUR = 1,4
               PRINT*, ' INPUT CULTURE NUMBER, NUMBER OF CELLS,',
          +          ' DIAMETER OF DISH, AND RATE '
               READ (5,*) NUMBER, ICELLS, DIAMTR, RATE
               PRINT*
               PRINT*, '                   NUMBER OF CELLS    PETRI',
          +          ' DISH     GROWTH'
               PRINT*, 'CULTURE NUMBER     INTIALLY          ',
          +          'DIAMETER (CM)    RATE'
               PRINT 5, NUMBER, ICELLS, DIAMTR, RATE
         5     FORMAT (/,1X,5X,I4,12X,I4,14X,I3,12X,F5.2,/)
               PRINT*, 'GENERATION  NUMBER OF CELLS  % OF PETRI ',
          +          'DISH COVERED'
               PRINT*
      *
               CELLS = REAL(ICELLS)
```

117

```
                DO 15 GENERA = 1,5
                    CELLS = CELLS + CELLS*RATE
                    DISH = 3.141593*(REAL(DIAMTR)*10.0/2.0)**2
                    PERARE = CELLS/DISH*100.0
                    PRINT 10, GENERA, CELLS, PERARE
         10         FORMAT (1X,5X,I1,10X,F6.1,16X,F6.2)
         15     CONTINUE
     *
                PRINT*
         20 CONTINUE
     *
                END
     *------------------------------------------------------------*


26.  *------------------------------------------------------------*
            PROGRAM SERIES
     *
     *  This program uses a series to compute sine squared and
     *  compares the result with the intrinsic function's value.
     *
            REAL   X, SUM, TERM, SIN2, DIF
            INTEGER  I
     *
            PRINT*, ' ENTER X'
            READ(5,*) X
            PRINT*
            PRINT*, '          COMPARISON OF VALUES OF SINE SQUARED'
            PRINT*
            PRINT*, 'NUMBER        SERIES          INTRINSIC',
           +        '          ABSOLUTE'
            PRINT*, 'OF TERMS      SUMMATION        FUNCTION',
           +        ,          DIFFERENCE'
            PRINT*
     *
            TERM = X*X
            SUM = X*X
            SIN2 = SIN(X)**2
            DO 10 I = 2,14
               TERM = TERM*(-(2.0*X)**2)/(2.0*REAL(I)*
           +           (2.0*REAL(I)-1.0))

               SUM = SUM + TERM
               IF (MOD(I,2).EQ.0) THEN
                  DIF = ABS(SIN2-SUM)
                  PRINT 5, I, SUM, SIN2, DIF
         5        FORMAT (1X,2X,I2,10X,F7.4,9X,F7.4,8X,F7.4)
               ENDIF
         10 CONTINUE
     *
            END
     *------------------------------------------------------------*


27.  *------------------------------------------------------------*
            PROGRAM FACTOR
     *
```

```
     *   This program approximates the value n! using
     *   Stirling's formula.
     *
         INTEGER  N, NI
     *
         PRINT*, 'ENTER N WHERE N IS BETWEEN 1 AND 10'
         READ (5,*) N
         PRINT*
     *
       5 IF (N.GE.0) THEN
            IF (N.LE.10) THEN
               IF (N.EQ.0) THEN
                  NI = 1
               ELSE
                  NI = INT(SQRT(2.0*3.141593*REAL(N))*
       +                (REAL(N)/2.718282)**N+0.5)
               ENDIF
               PRINT 10, N, NI
      10       FORMAT (1X,I2,'! IS APPROXIMATELY ',I7,/)
            ELSE
               PRINT*, 'INPUT IS OUT OF RANGE'
               PRINT*
            ENDIF
            PRINT*, 'ENTER N WHERE N IS BETWEEN 1 AND 10'
            READ (5,*) N
            PRINT*
            GO TO 5
         ENDIF
     *
         END
```

28.

```
         PROGRAM DIODE
     *
     *   This program finds the current through a diode for
     *   varying voltages and temperatures.
     *
         REAL   ICUR, VOLT, ISAT, QCHAR, K, TEMP, FAREN
         INTEGER  I, J
     *
         ISAT = 1.0E-06
         K = 1.38E-23
         QCHAR = 1.6E-19
     *
         DO 20 I = 1,3
            IF (I.EQ.1) FAREN = 32.0
            IF (I.EQ.2) FAREN = 100.0
            IF (I.EQ.3) FAREN = 212.0
            TEMP = (FAREN - 32.0)*5.0/9.0 + 273.16
            PRINT 5, FAREN, TEMP
       5    FORMAT (1X,'JUNCTION TEMPERATURE = ',F6.2,' F = ',
       +            F6.2,' K',//,1X,'VOLTAGE ACROSS DIODE',10X,
       +            'CURRENT THROUGH DIODE')
            DO 15 J = -2,4
```

```
              VOLT = REAL(J)*0.125
              ICUR = ISAT*(EXP(QCHAR*VOLT/K/TEMP)-1.0)
              PRINT 10, VOLT, ICUR
10            FORMAT (1X,5X,F6.3,' V',21X,E11.4,' A')
15      CONTINUE
        PRINT*
20 CONTINUE
*
        END
*-----------------------------------------------------------*
```

Chapter 4

```
1.    *-----------------------------------------------------------*
           PROGRAM  QUALTY
      *
      *  This program uses defect data to print
      *  a Quality Analysis Report.
      *
           INTEGER  BOARDS, BDDEF, BDWIRE, BDIC, BDNON, WIRE,
          +         IC, NON, ID, NWIRE, NIC, NNON, DEFECT
      *
           BDDEF = 0
           BDWIRE = 0
           BDIC = 0
           BDNON = 0
           WIRE =0
           IC = 0
           NON = 0
           OPEN (UNIT=10,FILE='REPORT',STATUS='OLD')
           READ (10,*) BOARDS
      *
           PRINT*, '           MONTHLY QUALITY ANALYSIS REPORT'
           PRINT*
           PRINT*, 'IDENTIFICATION NUMBERS OF BOARDS WITH ',
          +        'THREE OR MORE DEFECTS:'
           PRINT*
      *
           READ (10,*) ID, NWIRE, NIC, NNON
       10  IF (ID.NE.99999) THEN
              IF (ID.GT.5000) THEN
                 PRINT 12, ID
       12        FORMAT (1X,'ERROR IN ID:',I8)
              ENDIF
              IF (NWIRE + NIC + NNON.GE.3) PRINT 15, ID
       15     FORMAT (1X,I8)
              BDDEF = BDDEF + 1
              IF (NWIRE.GT.0) BDWIRE = BDWIRE + 1
              IF (NIC.GT.0) BDIC = BDIC + 1
              IF (NNON.GT.0) BDNON = BDNON + 1
              WIRE = WIRE + NWIRE
              IC = IC + NIC
              NON = NON + NNON
              READ(10,*) ID, NWIRE, NIC, NNON
              GO TO 10
           ENDIF
      *
           PRINT*
           PRINT 20, BOARDS
       20  FORMAT (1X,'TOTAL NUMBER OF BOARDS ASSEMBLED = ',I4)
           PRINT*
           PRINT 25, BDDEF
       25  FORMAT (1X,'TOTAL BOARDS WITH DEFECTS = ',I4)
           PRINT*
           PRINT 30, BDWIRE
       30  FORMAT (1X,5X,I4,' BOARDS WITH BROKEN WIRES')
```

121

```
      PRINT 35, BDIC
35 FORMAT (1X,5X,I4,' BOARDS WITH DEFECTIVE',
   +          ' IC COMPONENTS')
      PRINT 40, BDNON
40 FORMAT (1X,5X,I4,' BOARDS WITH DEFECTIVE',
   +          ' NON-IC COMPONENTS')
      PRINT*
      PRINT 45
45 FORMAT (1X,'DEFECT ANALYSIS')
      PRINT*
      DEFECT = WIRE + IC + NON
      PRINT 50, REAL(WIRE)*100.0/REAL(DEFECT)
50 FORMAT (1X,5X,F5.1,'% DEFECTS ARE BROKEN WIRES')
      PRINT 55, REAL(IC)*100.0/REAL(DEFECT)
55 FORMAT (1X,5X,F5.1,'% OF DEFECTS ARE DEFECTIVE',
   +          ' IC COMPONENTS')
      PRINT 60, REAL(NON)*100.0/REAL(DEFECT)
60 FORMAT (1X,5X,F5.1,'% OF DEFECTS ARE DEFECTIVE',
   +          ' NON-IC COMPONENTS')
*
      END
*-----------------------------------------------------------*

2.    *-----------------------------------------------------------*
      PROGRAM  QUALTY
*
*  This program uses defect data to print
*  a Quality Analysis Report.
*
      INTEGER  BOARDS, BDDEF, BDWIRE, BDIC, BDNON, WIRE,
   +           IC, NON, ID, NWIRE, NIC, NNON, DEFECT
*
      BDDEF = 0
      BDWIRE = 0
      BDIC = 0
      BDNON = 0
      WIRE =0
      IC = 0
      NON = 0
      OPEN (UNIT=10,FILE='REPORT',STATUS='OLD')
      READ (10,*) BOARDS
*
      PRINT*, '           MONTHLY QUALITY ANALYSIS REPORT'
      PRINT*
      PRINT*, 'IDENTIFICATION NUMBERS OF BOARDS WITH ',
   +          'THREE OR MORE DEFECTS:'
      PRINT*
*
      READ (10,*) ID, NWIRE, NIC, NNON
10 IF (ID.NE.99999) THEN
      IF (NWIRE + NIC + NNON.GE.3) PRINT 15, ID
15    FORMAT (1X,I8)
      BDDEF = BDDEF + 1
      IF (NWIRE.GT.0) BDWIRE = BDWIRE + 1
      IF (NIC.GT.0) BDIC = BDIC + 1
```

```
             IF (NNON.GT.0) BDNON = BDNON + 1
             WIRE = WIRE + NWIRE
             IC = IC + NIC
             NON = NON + NNON
             READ(10,*) ID, NWIRE, NIC, NNON
             GO TO 10
         ENDIF
*

         PRINT*
         PRINT 20, BOARDS
      20 FORMAT (1X,'TOTAL NUMBER OF BOARDS ASSEMBLED = ',I4)
         PRINT*
         PRINT 25, BDDEF
      25 FORMAT (1X,'TOTAL BOARDS WITH DEFECTS = ',I4)
         PRINT 28, REAL(BDDEF)*100.0/REAL(BOARDS)
      28 FORMAT (1X,'PERCENT OF BOARDS WITH DEFECTS = ',F6.2)
         PRINT*
         PRINT 30, BDWIRE
      30 FORMAT (1X,5X,I4,' BOARDS WITH BROKEN WIRES')
         PRINT 35, BDIC
      35 FORMAT (1X,5X,I4,' BOARDS WITH DEFECTIVE',
         +         ' IC COMPONENTS')
         PRINT 40, BDNON
      40 FORMAT (1X,5X,I4,' BOARDS WITH DEFECTIVE',
         +         ' NON-IC COMPONENTS')
         PRINT*
         PRINT 45
      45 FORMAT (1X,'DEFECT ANALYSIS')
         PRINT*
         DEFECT = WIRE + IC + NON
         PRINT 50, REAL(WIRE)*100.0/REAL(DEFECT)
      50 FORMAT (1X,5X,F5.1,'% DEFECTS ARE BROKEN WIRES')
         PRINT 55, REAL(IC)*100.0/REAL(DEFECT)
      55 FORMAT (1X,5X,F5.1,'% OF DEFECTS ARE DEFECTIVE',
         +         ' IC COMPONENTS')
         PRINT 60, REAL(NON)*100.0/REAL(DEFECT)
      60 FORMAT (1X,5X,F5.1,'% OF DEFECTS ARE DEFECTIVE',
         +         ' NON-IC COMPONENTS')
*

         END
*------------------------------------------------------------*

3.  Solution in text.

4.  *------------------------------------------------------------*
         PROGRAM  QUALTY
*
*  This program uses defect data to print
*  a Quality Analysis Report.
*
         INTEGER  BOARDS, BDDEF, BDWIRE, BDIC, BDNON, WIRE,
         +         IC, NON, ID, NWIRE, NIC, NNON, DEFECT,
         +         TOTIN, TOTOUT
*
         BDDEF = 0
```

```
      BDWIRE = 0
      BDIC = 0
      BDNON = 0
      WIRE =0
      IC = 0
      NON = 0
      OPEN (UNIT=10,FILE='REPORT',STATUS='OLD')
      READ (10,*) BOARDS
*
      PRINT*, '            MONTHLY QUALITY ANALYSIS REPORT'
      PRINT*
      PRINT*, 'IDENTIFICATION NUMBERS OF BOARDS WITH ',
     +        'THREE OR MORE DEFECTS:'
      PRINT*
*
      READ (10,*) ID, NWIRE, NIC, NNON
   10 IF (ID.NE.99999) THEN
         TOTIN = BDWIRE + BDIC + BDNON
         IF (NWIRE + NIC + NNON.GE.3) PRINT 15, ID
   15    FORMAT (1X,I8)
         BDDEF = BDDEF + 1
         IF (NWIRE.GT.0) BDWIRE = BDWIRE + 1
         IF (NIC.GT.0) BDIC = BDIC + 1
         IF (NNON.GT.0) BDNON = BDNON + 1
         WIRE = WIRE + NWIRE
         IC = IC + NIC
         NON = NON + NNON
         TOTOUT = BDWIRE + BDIC + BDNON
         IF (TOTOUT - TOTIN.GE.2) THEN
            PRINT 17, ID
   17       FORMAT (1X,'BOARD NO. ',I8,' HAS DEFECTS IN',
     +              ' TWO OR MORE CATEGORIES')
         ENDIF
         READ(10,*) ID, NWIRE, NIC, NNON
         GO TO 10
      ENDIF
*
      PRINT*
      PRINT 20, BOARDS
   20 FORMAT (1X,'TOTAL NUMBER OF BOARDS ASSEMBLED = ',I4)
      PRINT*
      PRINT 25, BDDEF
   25 FORMAT (1X,'TOTAL BOARDS WITH DEFECTS = ',I4)
      PRINT*
      PRINT 30, BDWIRE
   30 FORMAT (1X,5X,I4,' BOARDS WITH BROKEN WIRES')
      PRINT 35, BDIC
   35 FORMAT (1X,5X,I4,' BOARDS WITH DEFECTIVE',
     +        ' IC COMPONENTS')
      PRINT 40, BDNON
   40 FORMAT (1X,5X,I4,' BOARDS WITH DEFECTIVE',
     +        ' NON-IC COMPONENTS')
      PRINT*
      PRINT 45
   45 FORMAT (1X,'DEFECT ANALYSIS')
```

124

```
      PRINT*
      DEFECT = WIRE + IC + NON
      PRINT 50, REAL(WIRE)*100.0/REAL(DEFECT)
   50 FORMAT (1X,5X,F5.1,'% DEFECTS ARE BROKEN WIRES')
      PRINT 55, REAL(IC)*100.0/REAL(DEFECT)
   55 FORMAT (1X,5X,F5.1,'% OF DEFECTS ARE DEFECTIVE',
     +          ' IC COMPONENTS')
      PRINT 60, REAL(NON)*100.0/REAL(DEFECT)
   60 FORMAT (1X,5X,F5.1,'% OF DEFECTS ARE DEFECTIVE',
     +          ' NON-IC COMPONENTS')
*
      END
*------------------------------------------------------------*
```

5.
```
*------------------------------------------------------------*
      PROGRAM  QUALTY
*
*  This program uses defect data to print
*  a Quality Analysis Report.
*
      INTEGER  BOARDS, BDDEF, BDWIRE, BDIC, BDNON, WIRE,
     +         IC, NON, ID, NWIRE, NIC, NNON, DEFECT, TOT,
     +         DEF1, DEF2, DEF3, DEFGR3
*
      BDDEF = 0
      BDWIRE = 0
      BDIC = 0
      BDNON = 0
      WIRE =0
      IC = 0
      NON = 0
      DEF1 = 0
      DEF2 = 0
      DEF3 = 0
      DEFGR3 = 0
      OPEN (UNIT=10,FILE='REPORT',STATUS='OLD')
      READ (10,*) BOARDS
*
      PRINT*, '             MONTHLY QUALITY ANALYSIS REPORT'
      PRINT*
      PRINT*, 'IDENTIFICATION NUMBERS OF BOARDS WITH ',
     +          'THREE OR MORE DEFECTS:'
      PRINT*
*
      READ (10,*) ID, NWIRE, NIC, NNON
   10 IF (ID.NE.99999) THEN
         TOT = NWIRE + NIC + NNON
         IF (TOT.EQ.1) THEN
            DEF1 = DEF1 + 1
         ELSEIF (TOT.EQ.2) THEN
            DEF2 = DEF2 + 1
         ELSEIF (TOT.EQ.3) THEN
            DEF3 = DEF3 + 1
         ELSEIF (TOT.GT.3) THEN
            DEFGR3 = DEFGR3 + 1
```

```
         ENDIF
         IF (TOT.GE.3) PRINT 15, ID
    15   FORMAT (1X,I8)
         BDDEF = BDDEF + 1
         IF (NWIRE.GT.0) BDWIRE = BDWIRE + 1
         IF (NIC.GT.0) BDIC = BDIC + 1
         IF (NNON.GT.0) BDNON = BDNON + 1
         WIRE = WIRE + NWIRE
         IC = IC + NIC
         NON = NON + NNON
         READ(10,*) ID, NWIRE, NIC, NNON
         GO TO 10
      ENDIF
*

      PRINT*
      PRINT 20, BOARDS
   20 FORMAT (1X,'TOTAL NUMBER OF BOARDS ASSEMBLED = ',I4)
      PRINT*
      PRINT 25, BDDEF
   25 FORMAT (1X,'TOTAL BOARDS WITH DEFECTS = ',I4)
      PRINT*
      PRINT 30, BDWIRE
   30 FORMAT (1X,5X,I4,' BOARDS WITH BROKEN WIRES')
      PRINT 35, BDIC
   35 FORMAT (1X,5X,I4,' BOARDS WITH DEFECTIVE',
     +          ' IC COMPONENTS')
      PRINT 40, BDNON
   40 FORMAT (1X,5X,I4,' BOARDS WITH DEFECTIVE',
     +          ' NON-IC COMPONENTS')
      PRINT*
      PRINT 45
   45 FORMAT (1X,'DEFECT ANALYSIS')
      PRINT*
      DEFECT = WIRE + IC + NON
      PRINT 50, REAL(WIRE)*100.0/REAL(DEFECT)
   50 FORMAT (1X,5X,F5.1,'% DEFECTS ARE BROKEN WIRES')
      PRINT 55, REAL(IC)*100.0/REAL(DEFECT)
   55 FORMAT (1X,5X,F5.1,'% OF DEFECTS ARE DEFECTIVE',
     +          ' IC COMPONENTS')
      PRINT 60, REAL(NON)*100.0/REAL(DEFECT)
   60 FORMAT (1X,5X,F5.1,'% OF DEFECTS ARE DEFECTIVE',
     +          ' NON-IC COMPONENTS')
      PRINT*
      PRINT 65, DEF1, DEF2
   65 FORMAT (1X,'BOARDS WITH 1 DEFECT:',I4,
     +          '; BOARDS WITH 2 DEFECTS:',I4)
      PRINT 70, DEF3, DEFGR3
   70 FORMAT (1X,'BOARDS WITH 3 DEFECTS:',I4,
     +          '; BOARDS WITH GREATER THAN 3 DEFECTS:',I4)
*
      END
*----------------------------------------------------------*

6. *----------------------------------------------------------*
      PROGRAM  CENSUS
```

```
*
*    This program reads 101 population values and determines
*    the years of smallest increase in population.
*
        INTEGER   YROLD, YRNEW, POPOLD, POPNEW, INCR, GRPOP,
       +          GRYR, YR1, YR2, I
*
        OPEN (UNIT=15,FILE='PEOPLE',STATUS='OLD')
        READ (15,*) YROLD, POPOLD
        GRPOP = 0
        DO 50 I=1,100
           READ (15,*) YRNEW, POPNEW
           INCR = REAL(POPNEW - POPOLD)/REAL(POPOLD)
           IF (I.EQ.1.OR.INCR.LT.GRPOP) THEN
              GRPOP = INCR
              GRYR = YRNEW
           ENDIF
           YROLD = YRNEW
           POPOLD = POPNEW
     50 CONTINUE
        YR1 = GRYR - 1
        YR2 = GRYR
        PRINT 55, YR1, YR2
     55 FORMAT (1X,'SMALLEST PERCENTAGE INCREASE OCCURRED',
       +          ' BETWEEN ',I4,' AND ',I4)
*
        END
*-------------------------------------------------------------*
```

7.   Solution in text.

8.
```
*-------------------------------------------------------------*
        PROGRAM   CENSUS
*
*    This program reads 101 population values and determines
*    the average increase in population.
*
        INTEGER   YROLD, YRNEW, POPOLD, POPNEW, INCR,
       +          I, TOT
        REAL   AVE
*
        OPEN (UNIT=15,FILE='PEOPLE',STATUS='OLD')
        READ (15,*) YROLD, POPOLD
        TOT = 0
        DO 50 I=1,100
           READ (15,*) YRNEW, POPNEW
           INCR = POPNEW - POPOLD
           TOT = TOT + INCR
           YROLD = YRNEW
           POPOLD = POPNEW
     50 CONTINUE
        AVE = REAL(TOT)/100.0
        PRINT 55, AVE
     55 FORMAT (1X,'AVERAGE INCREASE = ',F7.1)
*
```

```
      END
*----------------------------------------------------------*

9.    *----------------------------------------------------------*
      PROGRAM  CENSUS
*
*  This program reads 101 population values and determines
*  the years of greatest increase in population.
*
      INTEGER` YROLD, YRNEW, POPOLD, POPNEW, INCR, GRPOP,
     +         GRYR, YR1, YR2, I
*
      OPEN (UNIT=15,FILE='PEOPLE',STATUS='OLD')
      READ (15,*) YROLD, POPOLD
      GRPOP = 0
      DO 50 I=1,100
         READ (15,*) YRNEW, POPNEW
         INCR = POPNEW - POPOLD
         IF (I.EQ.1.OR.INCR.GT.GRPOP) THEN
            GRPOP = INCR
            GRYR = YRNEW
         ENDIF
         YROLD = YRNEW
         POPOLD = POPNEW
   50 CONTINUE
      YR1 = GRYR - 1
      YR2 = GRYR
      PRINT 55, YR1, YR2
   55 FORMAT (1X,'GREATEST INCREASE OCCURRED',
     +         ' BETWEEN ',I4,' AND ',I4)
*
      END
*----------------------------------------------------------*

10.   *----------------------------------------------------------*
      PROGRAM  CENSUS
*
*  This program reads 101 population values and determines
*  the years of smallest increase in population.
*
      INTEGER  YROLD, YRNEW, POPOLD, POPNEW, INCR, GRPOP,
     +         GRYR, YR1, YR2, I, POP1, POP2
*
      OPEN (UNIT=15,FILE='PEOPLE',STATUS='OLD')
      READ (15,*) YROLD, POPOLD
      GRPOP = 0
      DO 50 I=1,100
         READ (15,*) YRNEW, POPNEW
         INCR = POPNEW - POPOLD
         IF (I.EQ.1.OR.INCR.LT.GRPOP) THEN
            GRPOP = INCR
            GRYR = YRNEW
            POP2 = POPNEW
         ENDIF
         YROLD = YRNEW
```

```
              POPOLD = POPNEW
          50 CONTINUE
             YR1 = GRYR - 1
             YR2 = GRYR
             POP1 = POP2 - GRPOP
             PRINT 55, YR1, YR2
          55 FORMAT (1X,'SMALLEST INCREASE OCCURRED',
            +          ' BETWEEN ',I4,' AND ',I4)
             PRINT 60, YR1, POP1, YR2, POP2
          60 FORMAT (1X,'THE POPULATION IN ',I4,' WAS ',I4/
            +          1X,'THE POPULATION IN ',I4,' WAS ',I4)
      *
             END
      *------------------------------------------------------------*
```

11.
```
      *------------------------------------------------------------*
             PROGRAM  SOLAR
      *
      * This program computes average sum intensity
      * and average voltage produced by a photovoltaic cell.
      *
             INTEGER  NMEAS, TOTSUN, SUN, TIME
             REAL  TVOLT, VOLT, ASUN, AVOLT
      *
             NMEAS = 0
             TOTSUN = 0
             TVOLT = 0.0
             READ*, SUN, TIME, VOLT
           5 IF (SUN.NE.9999) THEN
                 TOTSUN = TOTSUN + SUN
                 TVOLT = TVOLT + VOLT
                 NMEAS = NMEAS + 1
                 READ*, SUN, TIME, VOLT
                 GO TO 5
             ENDIF
             ASUN = REAL(TOTSUN)/REAL(NMEAS)
             AVOLT = TVOLT/REAL(NMEAS)
             PRINT 10, NMEAS
          10 FORMAT (1X,'NUMBER OF MEASUREMENTS = ',I5)
             PRINT 15, ASUN, AVOLT
          15 FORMAT (1X,'AVERAGE SUN INTENSITY:'F6.2,3X,
            +          'AVERAGE VOLTAGE:',E11.4)
      *
             END
      *------------------------------------------------------------*
```

12.
```
      *------------------------------------------------------------*
             PROGRAM NUTRIT
      *
      * This program reads in initial and final weights and
      * computes the percentage increase.
      *
             INTEGER  N, ID, I
             REAL  BEGWT, FINWT, PERCNT
      *
```

```
          OPEN (UNIT=1,FILE='WEIGHTS',STATUS='OLD')
          READ (1,*) N
*

      IF (N.GE.1) THEN
          PRINT 5
    5     FORMAT (1X,21X,'NUTRITION STUDY',//,1X,5X,'ID',7X,
   +              'INITIAL WT',5X,'FINAL WT    PERCENT ',
   +              'INCREASE',/)
          DO 15 I = 1,N
              READ (1,*) ID, BEGWT, FINWT
              PERCNT = (FINWT - BEGWT)/BEGWT*100.0
              PRINT 10, N, ID, BEGWT, FINWT, PERCNT
   10         FORMAT (1X,I2,'. ',I3,8X,F5.1,10X,F5.1,10X,F6.2)
   15     CONTINUE
      ENDIF
*

      END
*------------------------------------------------------------*
```

13. Solution in text.

14.
```
*------------------------------------------------------------*
      PROGRAM TEMPER
*
*  This program reads in temperatures of two compounds and
*  prints them in a table.
*
      INTEGER  MIN, HOUR, TEMP1, TEMP2
*
      OPEN (UNIT=1,FILE='TEMP',STATUS='OLD')
*
      PRINT 5
    5 FORMAT (1X,5X,'TEMPERATURE MEASUREMENTS',//,1X,5X,
   +         'TIME ELAPSED',/,1X,5X,'HOURS AND MINUTES',8X,
   +         'COMPOUND 1     COMPOUND 2',//)
*
      DO 20 HOUR = 0,7
          DO 15 MIN = 0,40,20
              READ (1,*) TEMP1, TEMP2
              PRINT 10, HOUR, MIN, TEMP1, TEMP2
   10         FORMAT(1X,7X,I1,9X,I2,13X,I5,9X,I5)
   15     CONTINUE
   20 CONTINUE
*
      END
*------------------------------------------------------------*
```

15.
```
*------------------------------------------------------------*
      PROGRAM TEMPER
*
*  This program reads in temperatures of two compounds and
*  finds the minimum temperature for each compound.
*
      INTEGER  MIN, HOUR, LESH1, LESH2, LSMIN1, LSMIN2, I,
   +           TEMP1, TEMP2, LESS1, LESS2
```

```
*
      OPEN (UNIT=1,FILE='TEMP',STATUS='OLD')
*
      LESS1 = 999999
      LESS2 = 999999
      PRINT 5
    5 FORMAT (1X,5X,'TEMPERATURE MEASUREMENTS',//,1X,5X,
   +         'TIME ELAPSED',/,1X,5X,'HOURS AND MINUTES',8X,
   +         'COMPOUND 1     COMPOUND 2',//)
*
      DO 20 HOUR = 0,7
         DO 15 MIN = 0,40,20
            READ (1,*) TEMP1, TEMP2
            IF (TEMP1.LT.LESS1) THEN
               LESS1 = TEMP1
               LESH1 = HOUR
               LSMIN1 = MIN
            ENDIF
            IF (TEMP2.LT.LESS2) THEN
               LESS2 = TEMP2
               LESH2 = HOUR
               LSMIN2 = MIN
            ENDIF
            PRINT 10, HOUR, MIN, TEMP1, TEMP2
   10       FORMAT(1X,7X,I1,9X,I2,13X,I5,9X,I5)
   15    CONTINUE
   20 CONTINUE
*
      I = 1
      PRINT 25, I,LESS1,LESH1,LSMIN1,I+1,LESS2,LESH2,LSMIN2
   25 FORMAT (//,1X,'MINIMUM TEMPERATURE AND TIME ELAPSED ',
   +         '(HOURS AND MINUTES)',/,2(1X,5X,'COMPOUND ',
   +         I1,7X,I5,12X,I2,8X,I2,/))
*
      END
*-------------------------------------------------------*

16. *-------------------------------------------------------*
      PROGRAM PAY
*
* This program computes the salaries of employees according
* to number of hours worked.
*
      INTEGER ID
      REAL  HOURS, RATE, PAYCHK
*
      OPEN (UNIT=1,FILE='WEEKLY',STATUS='OLD')
      PRINT*, '          PAYROLL FOR THIS WEEK'
      PRINT*, '      EMPLOYEE ID#        PAYCHECK'
      PRINT*
*
    5 READ (1,*,END=15) ID, HOURS, RATE
         IF (HOURS.LE.40.0) THEN
            PAYCHK = HOURS*RATE
         ELSEIF (HOURS.LE.50.0) THEN
```

131

```
                PAYCHK = 40.0*RATE
                PAYCHK = PAYCHK + (HOURS - 40)*RATE*1.5
            ELSE
                PAYCHK = 40.0*RATE + 10.0*RATE*1.5
                PAYCHK = PAYCHK + (HOURS - 50.0)*RATE*2.0
            ENDIF
            PRINT 10, ID, PAYCHK
      10    FORMAT (1X,11X,I4,11X'$',F8.2)
            GO TO 5
      15 CONTINUE
*
        END
*------------------------------------------------------------*

17.  *------------------------------------------------------------*
        PROGRAM FUEL
*
*  This program conputes fuel costs for an automobile.
*
        REAL  MILE1, MILE2, COST, GALLON, CPM, MPG, DMILE
*
        OPEN (UNIT=1,FILE='MILES',STATUS='OLD')
        PRINT 5
      5 FORMAT (1X,19X,'FUEL COST INFORMATION',//,1X,'MILES',5X,
     +    'GALLONS',5X,'COST',5X,'COST/MILE',5X,'MILES/GALLON')
        READ (1,*) MILE1
        READ (1,*) MILE2, COST, GALLON
*
      10 IF (MILE2.GT.0.0) THEN
            DMILE = MILE2 - MILE1
            CPM = COST/DMILE
            MPG = DMILE/GALLON
            PRINT 15, DMILE, GALLON, COST, CPM, MPG
      15    FORMAT (1X,F5.1,7X,F4.1,6X,F5.2,7X,F4.2,11X,F4.1)
            MILE1 = MILE2
            READ (1,*) MILE2, COST, GALLON
            GO TO 10
        ENDIF
*    /
        END
*------------------------------------------------------------*
18.  *------------------------------------------------------------*
        PROGRAM FUEL
*
*  This program conputes fuel costs for an automobile.
*
        REAL  MILE1, MILE2, COST, GALLON, CPM, MPG, DMILE,
     +        TOTMIL, TOTCOS, TOTGAL, AVGCPM, AVGMPG
*
        TOTMIL = 0.0
        TOTCOS = 0.0
        TOTGAL = 0.0
*
        OPEN (UNIT=1,FILE='MILES',STATUS='OLD')
        PRINT 5
```

```
    5 FORMAT (1X,19X,'FUEL COST INFORMATION',//,1X,'MILES',5X,
   +    'GALLONS',5X,'COST',5X,'COST/MILE',5X,'MILES/GALLON')
      READ (1,*) MILE1
      READ (1,*) MILE2, COST, GALLON
*
   10 IF (MILE2.GT.0.0) THEN
         DMILE = MILE2 - MILE1
         TOTMIL = TOTMIL + DMILE
         TOTCOS = TOTCOS + COST
         TOTGAL = TOTGAL + GALLON
         CPM = COST/DMILE
         MPG = DMILE/GALLON
         PRINT 15, DMILE, GALLON, COST, CPM, MPG
   15    FORMAT (1X,F5.1,7X,F4.1,6X,F5.2,7X,F4.2,11X,F4.1)
         MILE1 = MILE2
         READ (1,*) MILE2, COST, GALLON
         GO TO 10
      ENDIF
      AVGCPM = TOTCOS/TOTMIL
      AVGMPG = TOTMIL/TOTGAL
      PRINT 20, TOTMIL, TOTCOS, TOTGAL, AVGCPM, AVGMPG
   20 FORMAT (1X,6X,'SUMMARY INFORMATION',//,1X,'TOTAL MILES',
   +         14X,F6.1,/,1X,'TOTAL COST',13X,F8.2,/,1X,
   +         'TOTAL GALLONS',12X,F6.1,/,1X,'AVERAGE COST/MILE',
   +         10X,F4.2,/,1X,'AVERAGE MILE/GALLON',8X,F4.1)
*
      END
*-------------------------------------------------------------*

19. *-------------------------------------------------------------*
      PROGRAM DRILL
*
*  This program calculates the number of sticks of explosives
*  needed at a site.
*
      INTEGER  SITES, ID, DEPTH, BOOM, STICKS, I
      REAL   CHARGE
*
      OPEN (UNIT=1,FILE='DRILL',STATUS='OLD')
*
      READ (1,*) SITES
      PRINT 5
    5 FORMAT (1X,17X,'DAILY DRILLING REPORT',//,1X,'SITE ID',3X,
   +         'DEPTH   IDEAL POWDER   ACTUAL POWDER   STICKS',/,
   +         1X,10X,'(FT)    CHARGE (LBS)   CHARGE (LBS)',/,1X,
   +         7('-'),3X,5('-'),3X,12('-'),3X,13('-'),3X,6('-'))
*
      DO 15 I = 1,SITES
         READ (1,*) ID, DEPTH
         CHARGE = REAL(DEPTH)/(3.0*2.5)*5.0
         BOOM = INT(CHARGE-MOD(CHARGE,5.0)+.01)
         STICKS = BOOM/5
         PRINT 10, ID, DEPTH, CHARGE, BOOM, STICKS
   10    FORMAT (1X,1X,I5,5X,I3,6X,F8.4,10X,I3,9X,I3)
   15 CONTINUE
```

```
      *
            END
      *-----------------------------------------------------------------*


20.   *-----------------------------------------------------------------*
            PROGRAM DRILL
      *
      *  This program calculates the number of sticks of explosives
      *  needed at a site.
      *
            INTEGER  SITES, ID, DEPTH, BOOM, STICKS, I, TOTPOW,
           +           TOTSTI, TOTFT
            REAL  CHARGE
      *
            OPEN (UNIT=1,FILE='DRILL',STATUS='OLD')
      *
            TOTPOW = 0
            TOTSTI = 0
            TOTFT = 0
      *
            READ (1,*) SITES
            PRINT 5
          5 FORMAT (1X,17X,'DAILY DRILLING REPORT',//,1X,'SITE ID',3X,
           +          'DEPTH   IDEAL POWDER   ACTUAL POWDER   STICKS',/,
           +          1X,10X,'(FT)    CHARGE (LBS)   CHARGE (LBS)',/,1X,
           +          7('-'),3X,5('-'),3X,12('-'),3X,13('-'),3X,6('-'))
      *
            DO 15 I = 1,SITES
               READ (1,*) ID, DEPTH
               CHARGE = REAL(DEPTH)/3.0/2.5*5.0
               BOOM = INT(CHARGE-MOD(CHARGE,5.0)+.01)
               STICKS = BOOM/5
               TOTPOW = TOTPOW + BOOM
               TOTSTI = TOTSTI + STICKS
               TOTFT = TOTFT + DEPTH
               PRINT 10, ID, DEPTH, CHARGE, BOOM, STICKS
         10    FORMAT (1X,1X,I5,5X,I3,6X,F8.4,10X,I3,9X,I3)
         15 CONTINUE
      *
            PRINT 20, TOTPOW, TOTSTI, TOTFT
         20 FORMAT (//,1X,5X,'TOTAL POWDER USED = ',I5,' LBS  (',I4,
           +    ' STICKS)',/,6X,'TOTAL DRILLING FOOTAGE = ',I6,' FT')
      *
            END
      *-----------------------------------------------------------------*


21.   *-----------------------------------------------------------------*
            PROGRAM DRILL
      *
      *  This program calculates the number of sticks of
      *  explosives needed at a site.
      *
            INTEGER  SITES, ID, DEPTH, BOOM, STICKS, I, TOTPOW,
           +           TOTSTI, TOTFT, HOLES
            REAL  CHARGE
```

```
*
            OPEN (UNIT=1,FILE='DRILL',STATUS='OLD')
*
            TOTPOW = 0
            TOTSTI = 0
            TOTFT = 0
            HOLES = 0
*
            READ (1,*) SITES
            PRINT 5
        5 FORMAT (1X,17X,'DAILY DRILLING REPORT',//,1X,'SITE ID',3X,
            +        'DEPTH   IDEAL POWDER    ACTUAL POWDER    STICKS',/,
            +        1X,10X,'(FT)    CHARGE (LBS)    CHARGE (LBS)',/,1X,
            +        7('-'),3X,5('-'),3X,12('-'),3X,13('-'),3X,6('-'))
*
            DO 20 I = 1,SITES
                READ (1,*) ID, DEPTH
                IF (DEPTH.GE.30) THEN
                    CHARGE = REAL(DEPTH)/3.0/2.5*5.0
                    BOOM = INT(CHARGE-MOD(CHARGE,5.0)+.01)
                    STICKS = BOOM/5
                    TOTPOW = TOTPOW + BOOM
                    TOTSTI = TOTSTI + STICKS
                    TOTFT = TOTFT + DEPTH
                    PRINT 10, ID, DEPTH, CHARGE, BOOM, STICKS
        10          FORMAT (1X,1X,I5,5X,I3,6X,F8.4,10X,I3,9X,I3)
                ELSE
                    HOLES = HOLES + 1
                    PRINT 15, ID, DEPTH
        15          FORMAT (1X,1X,I5,5X,I3,6X,'HOLE TOO SHALLOW'
            +                ' FOR BLASTING')
                ENDIF
        20 CONTINUE
*
            PRINT 25, TOTPOW, TOTSTI, TOTFT, HOLES
        25 FORMAT (//,1X,5X,'TOTAL POWDER USED = ',I5,' LBS  (',I4,
            +        ' STICKS)',/,6X,'TOTAL DRILLING FOOTAGE = ',I6,
            +        ' FT',/,5X,'NUMBER OF HOLES TOO SHALLOW',I3)
*
            END
*-----------------------------------------------------------*
```

22.
```
*-----------------------------------------------------------*
        PROGRAM BEAMS
*
* This program computes the load that can be applied to a beam.
*
        INTEGER  BEAMNM
        REAL   DEFLCT, LOAD, ALEN, ELASTC, MOMENT, BASE, HEIGHT,
        +        BEAMLE
*
        OPEN (UNIT=1,FILE='BEAMS',STATUS='OLD')
*
        DO 20 BEAMNM = 1,5
            READ (1,*) BEAMLE, BASE, HEIGHT, ELASTC, LOAD
```

135

```
            PRINT 5, BEAMNM, BEAMLE
      5     FORMAT (//,1X,'BEAM NO. ',I1,'   TOTAL LENGTH = ',F6.2,
     +          ' FT',//,1X,5X,'DISTANCE OF LOAD FROM FIXED END',
     +          7X,'DEFLECTION')
            ALEN = 1.0
*
      10    IF (ALEN.LE.BEAMLE) THEN
               MOMENT = (BASE*HEIGHT**3)/12.0
               DEFLCT = ((LOAD*ALEN**2)/(2.0*ELASTC*MOMENT))*
     +               (BEAMLE - ALEN/3.0)
               PRINT 15, ALEN, DEFLCT
      15       FORMAT (1X,15X,F6.2,24X,F6.2)
               ALEN = ALEN + 1.0
               GO TO 10
            ENDIF
*
      20 CONTINUE
*
         END
*-----------------------------------------------------------*
```

23.
```
*-----------------------------------------------------------*
         PROGRAM BEAMS
*
* This program computes the load that can be applied to a beam
* as long as the deflection is no more than 5% of beam length.
*
         INTEGER  BEAMNM, FLAG
         REAL  DEFLCT, LOAD, ALEN, ELASTC, MOMENT, BASE, HEIGHT,
     +        BEAMLE, FIVEPC
*
         OPEN (UNIT=1,FILE='BEAMS',STATUS='OLD')
*
         DO 20 BEAMNM = 1,5
            READ (1,*) BEAMLE, BASE, HEIGHT, ELASTC, LOAD
            FIVEPC = BEAMLE*0.05
            PRINT 5, BEAMNM, BEAMLE, FIVEPC
      5     FORMAT (//,1X,'BEAM NO. ',I1,'   TOTAL LENGTH = ',F6.2,
     +          ' FT',/,1X,13X,'5% OF LENGTH = ',F6.2,' FT',/,1X,
     +          5X,'DISTANCE OF LOAD FROM FIXED END',7X,
     +          'DEFLECTION')
            ALEN = 1.0
            FLAG = 0
*
      10    IF ((ALEN.LE.BEAMLE).AND.(FLAG.EQ.0)) THEN
               MOMENT = (BASE*HEIGHT**3)/12.0
               DEFLCT = ((LOAD*ALEN**2)/(2.0*ELASTC*MOMENT))*
     +               (BEAMLE - ALEN/3.0)
               IF (DEFLCT.GE.FIVEPC) THEN
                  FLAG = 1
               ELSE
                  PRINT 15, ALEN, DEFLCT
      15          FORMAT (1X,15X,F6.2,24X,F6.2)
                  ALEN = ALEN + 1.0
               ENDIF
```

```
                GO TO 10
            ENDIF
            IF (FLAG.EQ.0) THEN
                PRINT*
                PRINT*, '                   DEFLECTION OF 5% OF',
     +                   'LENGTH NOT REACHED'
            ENDIF
*
     20 CONTINUE
*
        END
*----------------------------------------------------------------*
```

24.
```
*----------------------------------------------------------------*
        PROGRAM CONVRT
*
*   This program creates a new file of polar coordinates from
*   an old file containing rectangular coordinates.
*
        INTEGER  I, COUNT
        REAL   THETA, RAD, X, Y
*
        OPEN (UNIT=1,FILE='DATAXY',STATUS='OLD')
        OPEN (UNIT=2,FILE='POLAR',STATUS='NEW')
*
        READ (1,*) COUNT
        WRITE (2,*) COUNT
*
        DO 5 I = 1,COUNT
            READ (1,*) X, Y
            RAD = SQRT(X**2 + Y**2)
            THETA = ATAN2(Y,X)
            WRITE (2,*) RAD, THETA
      5 CONTINUE
*
        END
*----------------------------------------------------------------*
```

25.
```
*----------------------------------------------------------------*
        PROGRAM CONVRT
*
*   This program converts polar coordinates to rectangular.
*
        INTEGER  I, COUNT
        REAL   RAD, THETA, X, Y
x
        OPEN (UNIT=1,FILE='POLAR',STATUS='OLD')
        OPEN (UNIT=2,FILE='DATAXY',STATUS='NEW')
*
        READ (1,*) COUNT
        WRITE (2,*) COUNT
*
        DO 5 I = 1,COUNT
            READ (1,*) RAD, THETA
            X = RAD*COS(THETA)
```

```
              Y = RAD*SIN(THETA)
              WRITE (2,*) X, Y
        5 CONTINUE
  *

        END
  *------------------------------------------------------------*


26.   *------------------------------------------------------------*

        PROGRAM CONVRT
  *
  *  This program converts rectangular coordinates to polar.
  *
        INTEGER  I, COUNT
        REAL   THETA, RAD, X, Y
  *
        OPEN (UNIT=1,FILE='DATAXY',STATUS='OLD')
        OPEN (UNIT=2,FILE='DATA',STATUS='NEW')
  *
        READ (1,*) COUNT
        WRITE (2,*) COUNT
  *
        DO 5 I = 1,COUNT
            READ (1,*) X, Y
            RAD = SQRT(X**2 + Y**2)
            THETA = ATAN2(Y,X)
            WRITE (2,*) X, Y, RAD, THETA
        5 CONTINUE
  *
        END
  *------------------------------------------------------------*
```

Chapter 5

1.   Solution in text.

2.   *--*
```
      PROGRAM  SNOFAL
*
*  This program computes the average snowfall
*  for January and counts the number of days
*  with above-average snowfall.
*
      INTEGER  COUNT, MINCT, I
      REAL  SNOW(31), TOTAL, AVE, MAX
      DATA  TOTAL, COUNT, MIN, MINCT /0.0, 0, 0.0, 0/
*
      OPEN (UNIT=10,FILE='JAN',STATUS='OLD')
      READ (10,*) SNOW
      PRINT 5, SNOW
    5 FORMAT (1X,4F8.1)
*
      DO 10 I=1,31
         TOTAL = TOTAL + SNOW(I)
         IF (I.EQ.1) THEN
            MAX = SNOW(1)
         ELSE
            IF (MAX.LT.SNOW(I)) MAX = SNOW(I)
         ENDIF
   10 CONTINUE
      AVE = TOTAL/31.0
      PRINT 20, AVE
   20 FORMAT (1X,'AVERAGE SNOWFALL IS ',F5.2,' INCHES')
*
      DO 30 I=1,31
         IF (SNOW(I).GT.AVE) COUNT = COUNT + 1
         IF (SNOW(I).EQ.MAX) PRINT 25, I
   25    FORMAT (1X,'MAXIMUM SNOWFALL OCCURRED ON DAY ',I2)
   30 CONTINUE
      PRINT 40, COUNT
   40 FORMAT (1X,I2,' DAYS WITH ABOVE-AVERAGE SNOWFALL')
*
      END
```
      --

3.   *-----------------------   -------------------------------*
```
      PROGRAM  SNOFAL
*
*  This program computes the average snowfall
*  for January and counts the number of days
*  with above-average snowfall.
*
      INTEGER  COUNT, MINCT, I
      REAL  SNOW(31), TOTAL, AVE, MIN
      DATA  TOTAL, COUNT, MIN, MINCT /0.0, 0, 0.0, 0/
*
      OPEN (UNIT=10,FILE='JAN',STATUS='OLD')
```

139

```
      READ (10,*) SNOW
      PRINT 5, SNOW
    5 FORMAT (1X,4F8.1)
*
      DO 10 I=1,31
          TOTAL = TOTAL + SNOW(I)
          IF (SNOW(I).LT.MIN) MIN = SNOW(I)
   10 CONTINUE
      AVE = TOTAL/31.0
      PRINT 20, AVE
   20 FORMAT (1X,'AVERAGE SNOWFALL IS ',F5.2,' INCHES')
*
      DO 30 I=1,31
          IF (SNOW(I).GT.AVE) COUNT = COUNT + 1
          IF (SNOW(I).EQ.MIN) MINCT = MINCT + 1
   30 CONTINUE
      PRINT 40, COUNT
   40 FORMAT (1X,I2,' DAYS WITH ABOVE-AVERAGE SNOWFALL')
      PRINT 45, MIN
   45 FORMAT (1X,'MINIMUM SNOWFALL IS ',F5.2,' INCHES')
      PRINT 50, MINCT
   50 FORMAT (1X,I2,' DAYS WITH MINIMUM SNOWFALL')
*
      END
*----------------------------------------------------------*

4.    *----------------------------------------------------------*
      PROGRAM  SNOFAL
*
* This program computes the average snowfall
* for January and counts the number of days
* with above-average snowfall.
*
      INTEGER  COUNT, DAYS, MAX, I
      REAL  SNOW(31), TOTAL, AVE
      DATA  TOTAL, COUNT, DAYS, MAX /0.0, 0, 0, 0/
*
      OPEN (UNIT=10,FILE='JAN',STATUS='OLD')
      READ (10,*) SNOW
      PRINT 5, SNOW
    5 FORMAT (1X,4F8.1)
*
      DO 10 I=1,31
          TOTAL = TOTAL + SNOW(I)
          IF (SNOW(I).EQ.0.0) THEN
             DAYS = DAYS + 1
          ELSE
             IF (DAYS.GT.MAX) MAX = DAYS
             DAYS = 0
          ENDIF
   10 CONTINUE
      AVE = TOTAL/31.0
      PRINT 20, AVE
   20 FORMAT (1X,'AVERAGE SNOWFALL IS ',F5.2,' INCHES')
*
```

```
          DO 30 I=1,31
              IF (SNOW(I).GT.AVE) COUNT = COUNT + 1
       30 CONTINUE
          PRINT 40, COUNT
       40 FORMAT (1X,I2,' DAYS WITH ABOVE-AVERAGE SNOWFALL')
          PRINT 45, MAX
       45 FORMAT (1X,'LONGEST NUMBER OF CONSECUTIVE DAYS WITH ',
          +        'NO SNOWFALL = ',I3)
*
          END
*-------------------------------------------------------------*
```

5.
```
*-------------------------------------------------------------*
          PROGRAM  SNOFAL
*
*  This program computes the average snowfall
*  for January and counts the number of days
*  with above-average snowfall.
*
          INTEGER  COUNT, DAYS, MAX, I
          REAL  SNOW(31), TOTAL, AVE
          DATA  TOTAL, COUNT, DAYS, MAX /0.0, 0, 0, 0/
*
          OPEN (UNIT=10,FILE='JAN',STATUS='OLD')
          READ (10,*) SNOW
          PRINT 5, SNOW
        5 FORMAT (1X,4F8.1)
*
          DO 10 I=1,31
              TOTAL = TOTAL + SNOW(I)
              IF (SNOW(I).GT.0.0) THEN
                 DAYS = DAYS + 1
              ELSE
                 IF (DAYS.GT.MAX) MAX = DAYS
                 DAYS = 0
              ENDIF
       10 CONTINUE
          AVE = TOTAL/31.0
          PRINT 20, AVE
       20 FORMAT (1X,'AVERAGE SNOWFALL IS ',F5.2,' INCHES')
*
          DO 30 I=1,31
              IF (SNOW(I).GT.AVE) COUNT = COUNT + 1
       30 CONTINUE
          PRINT 40, COUNT
       40 FORMAT (1X,I2,' DAYS WITH ABOVE-AVERAGE SNOWFALL')
          PRINT 45, MAX
       45 FORMAT (1X,'LONGEST NUMBER OF CONSECUTIVE DAYS WITH ',
          +        'SNOWFALL = ',I3)
*
          END
*-------------------------------------------------------------*
```

6.
```
*-------------------------------------------------------------*
          PROGRAM  EARTH
```

```
*
*  This program will read a file of earthquake data
*  and sort and print it in ascending order.
*
      INTEGER  LOCATE, I, N
      REAL  QUAKE(200), TEMP
      LOGICAL  SORTED
*
      OPEN (UNIT=9,FILE='MOTION',STATUS='OLD')
      READ(9,*) LOCATE
      PRINT 5, LOCATE
    5 FORMAT (1X,'LOCATION NUMBER: ',I5)
*
      I = 1
   10 READ (9,*,END=20) QUAKE(I)
         I = I + 1
         GO TO 10
*
   20 N = I - 1
      SORTED = .FALSE.
   30 IF (.NOT.SORTED) THEN
         SORTED = .TRUE.
         DO 40 I=1,N-1
            IF (QUAKE(I).LT.QUAKE(I+1)) THEN
               TEMP = QUAKE(I)
               QUAKE(I) = QUAKE(I+1)
               QUAKE(I+1) = TEMP
               SORTED = .FALSE.
            ENDIF
   40    CONTINUE
         GO TO 30
      ENDIF
*
      DO 60 I=1,N
         PRINT 50, I, QUAKE(I)
   50    FORMAT (1X,I3,'.',3X,F6.4)
   60 CONTINUE
*
      END
*------------------------------------------------------------*
```

7.
```
*------------------------------------------------------------*
      PROGRAM EARTH
*
*  This program will read a file of earthquake data
*  and sort and print it in ascending order.
*
      INTEGER  LOCATE, I, N
      REAL  QUAKE(200), TEMP, SUM, AVE
      LOGICAL  SORTED
*
      OPEN (UNIT=9,FILE='MOTION',STATUS='OLD')
      READ(9,*) LOCATE
      PRINT 5, LOCATE
    5 FORMAT (1X,'LOCATION NUMBER: ',I5)
```

```
*
      SUM = 0.0
      I = 1
   10 READ (9,*,END=20) QUAKE(I)
          SUM = SUM + QUAKE(I)
          I = I + 1
          GO TO 10
*
   20 N = I - 1
      SORTED = .FALSE.
   30 IF (.NOT.SORTED) THEN
          SORTED = .TRUE.
          DO 40 I=1,N-1
              IF (QUAKE(I).GT.QUAKE(I+1)) THEN
                  TEMP = QUAKE(I)
                  QUAKE(I) = QUAKE(I+1)
                  QUAKE(I+1) = TEMP
                  SORTED = .FALSE.
              ENDIF
   40     CONTINUE
          GO TO 30
      ENDIF
*
      DO 60 I=1,N
          PRINT 50, I, QUAKE(I)
   50     FORMAT (1X,I3,'.',3X,F6.4)
   60 CONTINUE
      AVE = SUM/REAL(N)
      PRINT 65, AVE
   65 FORMAT (1X,'AVERAGE EARTHQUAKE IS ',F6.4)
*
      END
*------------------------------------------------------------*


8.    *------------------------------------------------------------*
      PROGRAM  EARTH
*
* This program will read a file of earthquake data
* and sort and print it in ascending order.
*
      INTEGER  LOCATE, I, N
      REAL  QUAKE(200), TEMP
      LOGICAL  SORTED
*
      OPEN (UNIT=9,FILE='MOTION',STATUS='OLD')
      READ(9,*) LOCATE
      PRINT 5, LOCATE
    5 FORMAT (1X,'LOCATION NUMBER: ',I5)
*
      I = 1
   10 READ (9,*,END=20) QUAKE(I)
          I = I + 1
          GO TO 10
*
   20 N = I - 1
```

```
                 SORTED = .FALSE.
          30 IF (.NOT.SORTED) THEN
                 SORTED = .TRUE.
                 DO 40 I=1,N-1
                    IF (QUAKE(I).GT.QUAKE(I+1)) THEN
                       TEMP = QUAKE(I)
                       QUAKE(I) = QUAKE(I+1)
                       QUAKE(I+1) = TEMP
                       SORTED = .FALSE.
                    ENDIF
          40     CONTINUE
                 GO TO 30
             ENDIF
      *
             DO 60 I=1,N
                PRINT 50, I, QUAKE(I)
          50    FORMAT (1X,I3,'.',3X,F6.4)
          60 CONTINUE
             PRINT 65, QUAKE(N)
          65 FORMAT (1X,'MAXIMUM EARTHQUAKE IS ',F6.4)
      *
             END
      *-------------------------------------------------------*


9.  Solution in text.


10. *-------------------------------------------------------*
             PROGRAM  EARTH
      *
      * This program will read a file of earthquake data
      * and sort and print it in ascending order.
      *
             INTEGER  LOCATE, I, N, COUNT
             REAL  QUAKE(200), TEMP, ORIG(200)
             LOGICAL  SORTED
      *
             OPEN (UNIT=9,FILE='MOTION',STATUS='OLD')
             READ(9,*) LOCATE
             PRINT 5, LOCATE
           5 FORMAT (1X,'LOCATION NUMBER: ',I5)
      *
             I = 1
          10 READ (9,*,END=20) QUAKE(I)
                 ORIG(I) = QUAKE(I)
                 I = I + 1
                 GO TO 10
      *
          20 N = I - 1
             SORTED = .FALSE.
          30 IF (.NOT.SORTED) THEN
                 SORTED = .TRUE.
                 DO 40 I=1,N-1
                    IF (QUAKE(I).GT.QUAKE(I+1)) THEN
                       TEMP = QUAKE(I)
                       QUAKE(I) = QUAKE(I+1)
```

```
                  QUAKE(I+1) = TEMP
                  SORTED = .FALSE.
               ENDIF
40       CONTINUE
         GO TO 30
      ENDIF
*
      DO 60 I=1,N
         PRINT 50, I, QUAKE(I)
50       FORMAT (1X,I3,'.',3X,F6.4)
60 CONTINUE
*
      COUNT = 0
      DO 70 I=1,N
         IF (QUAKE(I).EQ.ORIG(I)) COUNT = COUNT + 1
70 CONTINUE
      PRINT 75, COUNT
75 FORMAT (1X,I4,' EARTHQUAKES IN SAME ',
     +          'POSITION BEFORE AND AFTER SORT')
*
      END
*---------------------------------------------------------------*


11.   *---------------------------------------------------------------*
      PROGRAM  PWRPLT
*
* This program computes and prints a composite report
* summarizing eight weeks of power plant data.
*
      INTEGER  POWER(8,7), MIN, TOTAL, COUNT, I, J
      REAL  AVE
      DATA  TOTAL, COUNT /0, 0/
*
      OPEN (UNIT=12,FILE='PLANT',STATUS='OLD')
      DO 5 I=1,8
         READ (12,*) (POWER(I,J), J=1,7)
  5 CONTINUE
*
      MIN = POWER(1,1)
      DO 15 I=1,8
         DO 10 J=1,7
            TOTAL = TOTAL + POWER(I,J)
            IF (POWER(I,J).LT.MIN) MIN = POWER(I,J)
10       CONTINUE
15 CONTINUE
      AVE = REAL(TOTAL)/56.0
*
      DO 25 I=1,8
         DO 20 J=1,7
            IF (POWER(I,J).GT.AVE) COUNT = COUNT + 1
20       CONTINUE
25 CONTINUE
*
      PRINT 30
30 FORMAT (1X,15X,'COMPOSITE INFORMATION')
```

```
      PRINT 35, AVE
   35 FORMAT (1X,'AVERAGE DAILY POWER OUTPUT = ',F5.1,
     +          ' MEGAWATTS')
      PRINT 40, COUNT
   40 FORMAT (1X,'NUMBER OF DAYS WITH GREATER THAN ',
     +          'AVERAGE POWER OUTPUT = ',I2)
      PRINT 45, MIN
   45 FORMAT (1X,'DAY(S) WITH MINIMUM POWER OUTPUT OF ',I5,':')
      DO 60 I=1,8
         DO 55 J=1,7
            IF (POWER(I,J).EQ.MIN) PRINT 50, I, J
   50       FORMAT (1X,12X,'WEEK ',I2,'   DAY ',I2)
   55    CONTINUE
   60 CONTINUE
*
      END
*----------------------------------------------------------------*

12.  *----------------------------------------------------------------*
      PROGRAM  PWRPLT
*
* This program computes and prints a composite report
* summarizing eight weeks of power plant data.
*
      INTEGER  POWER(8,7), MIN, MAX, TOTAL, COUNT, I, J
      REAL  AVE
      DATA  TOTAL, COUNT /0, 0/
*
      OPEN (UNIT=12,FILE='PLANT',STATUS='OLD')
      DO 5 I=1,8
         READ (12,*) (POWER(I,J), J=1,7)
    5 CONTINUE
*
      MIN = POWER(1,1)
      MAX = POWER(1,1)
      DO 15 I=1,8
         DO 10 J=1,7
            TOTAL = TOTAL + POWER(I,J)
            IF (POWER(I,J).LT.MIN) MIN = POWER(I,J)
            IF (POWER(I,J).GT.MAX) MAX = POWER(I,J)
   10    CONTINUE
   15 CONTINUE
      AVE = REAL(TOTAL)/56.0
*
      DO 25 I=1,8
         DO 20 J=1,7
            IF (POWER(I,J).GT.AVE) COUNT = COUNT + 1
   20    CONTINUE
   25 CONTINUE
*
      PRINT 30
   30 FORMAT (1X,15X,'COMPOSITE INFORMATION')
      PRINT 35, AVE
   35 FORMAT (1X,'AVERAGE DAILY POWER OUTPUT = ',F5.1,
     +          ' MEGAWATTS')
```

```
          PRINT 40, COUNT
       40 FORMAT (1X,'NUMBER OF DAYS WITH GREATER THAN ',
         +            'AVERAGE POWER OUTPUT = ',I2)
          PRINT 45, MIN, MAX
       45 FORMAT (1X,'MINIMUM POWER OUTPUT = ',I5,';',3X,
         +            'MAXIMUM POWER OUTPUT = ',I5)
       *
          END
*----------------------------------------------------------------*
```

13. Solution in text.

```
14. *----------------------------------------------------------------*
          PROGRAM  PWRPLT
       *
       * This program computes and prints a composite report
       * summarizing several weeks of power plant data.
       *
          INTEGER  POWER(8,7), MIN, MINCT, TOTAL, COUNT,
         +         I, J
          REAL  AVE
          DATA  TOTAL, COUNT, MINCT /0, 0, 0/
       *
          OPEN (UNIT=12,FILE='PLANT',STATUS='OLD')
          DO 5 I=1,8
             READ (12,*) (POWER(I,J), J=1,7)
        5 CONTINUE
       *
          MIN = POWER(1,1)
          DO 15 I=1,8
             DO 10 J=1,7
                TOTAL = TOTAL + POWER(I,J)
                IF (POWER(I,J).LT.MIN) MIN = POWER(I,J)
       10     CONTINUE
       15 CONTINUE
          AVE = REAL(TOTAL)/REAL(56.0)
       *
          DO 25 I=1,8
             DO 20 J=1,7
                IF (POWER(I,J).GT.AVE) COUNT = COUNT + 1
                IF (POWER(I,J).EQ.MIN) MINCT = MINCT + 1
       20     CONTINUE
       25 CONTINUE
       *
          PRINT 30
       30 FORMAT (1X,15X,'COMPOSITE INFORMATION')
          PRINT 35, AVE
       35 FORMAT (1X,'AVERAGE DAILY POWER OUTPUT = ',F5.1,
         +            ' MEGAWATTS')
          PRINT 40, COUNT
       40 FORMAT (1X,'NUMBER OF DAYS WITH GREATER THAN ',
         +            'AVERAGE POWER OUTPUT = ',I2)
          PRINT 45, MINCT
       45 FORMAT (1X,I3,1X,'DAY(S) WITH MINIMUM POWER OUTPUT')
       *
```

```
        END
*----------------------------------------------------------------*

15.  *----------------------------------------------------------------*
        PROGRAM  PWRPLT
*
*  This program computes and prints a composite report
*  summarizing eight weeks of power plant data.
*
        INTEGER  POWER(8,7), MIN, TOTAL, COUNT, I, J
        REAL  AVE, WKAVE
        DATA  TOTAL, COUNT /0, 0/
*
        OPEN (UNIT=12,FILE='PLANT',STATUS='OLD')
        DO 5 I=1,8
           READ (12,*) (POWER(I,J), J=1,7)
      5 CONTINUE
*
        MIN = POWER(1,1)
        DO 15 I=1,8
           DO 10 J=1,7
              TOTAL = TOTAL + POWER(I,J)
              IF (POWER(I,J).LT.MIN) MIN = POWER(I,J)
     10     CONTINUE
     15 CONTINUE
        AVE = REAL(TOTAL)/56.0
*
        DO 25 I=1,8
           WKAVE = 0.0
           DO 20 J=1,7
              IF (POWER(I,J).GT.AVE) COUNT = COUNT + 1
              WKAVE = WKAVE + POWER(I,J)
     20     CONTINUE
           PRINT 22, I, WKAVE/7.0
     22     FORMAT (1X,'AVERAGE FOR WEEK ',I4,' = ',F5.1)
     25 CONTINUE
*
        PRINT*
        PRINT 30
     30 FORMAT (1X,15X,'COMPOSITE INFORMATION')
        PRINT 35, AVE
     35 FORMAT (1X,'AVERAGE DAILY POWER OUTPUT = ',F5.1,
      +           ' MEGAWATTS')
        PRINT 40, COUNT
     40 FORMAT (1X,'NUMBER OF DAYS WITH GREATER THAN ',
      +           'AVERAGE POWER OUTPUT = ',I2)
        PRINT 45
     45 FORMAT (1X,'DAY(S) WITH MINIMUM POWER OUTPUT:')
        DO 60 I=1,8
           DO 55 J=1,7
              IF (POWER(I,J).EQ.MIN) PRINT 50, I, J
     50        FORMAT (1X,12X,'WEEK ',I2,'   DAY ',I2)
     55     CONTINUE
     60 CONTINUE
*
        END
```

148

```
      END
*-----------------------------------------------------------*


16. *-----------------------------------------------------------*
      PROGRAM  NAVIG
*
*  This program reads the elevation data for a set of land
*  grids and determines the number of peaks in each grid.
*
      INTEGER  MAP(100,100), I, J, N, ID, NROWS, NCOLS,
     +          COUNT
*
      PRINT 5
    5 FORMAT (1X,'SUMMARY OF LAND GRID ANALYSIS')
*
      OPEN (UNIT=15,FILE='ELEVTN',STATUS='OLD')
      READ (15,*) ID
      N = 0
   15 IF (ID.NE.99999) THEN
         READ (15,*) NROWS, NCOLS
         DO 20 I=1,NROWS
            READ (15,*) (MAP(I,J), J=1,NCOLS)
   20    CONTINUE
         COUNT = 0
         DO 30 I=2,NROWS-1
            DO 25 J=2,NCOLS-1
               IF ((MAP(I-1,J).LT.MAP(I,J)).AND.
     +             (MAP(I+1,J).LT.MAP(I,J)).AND.
     +             (MAP(I,J-1).LT.MAP(I,J)).AND.
     +             (MAP(I,J+1).LT.MAP(I,J))) THEN
                    COUNT = COUNT + 1
                    PRINT 22, I, J
   22               FORMAT (1X,'PEAK AT LOCATION: ',I3,',',I3)
               ENDIF
   25       CONTINUE
   30    CONTINUE
         PRINT 32
   32    FORMAT (1X,'IDENTIFICAITION  NUMBER OF POINTS    ',
     +           'NUMBER OF PEAKS')
         PRINT 35, ID, NROWS*NCOLS, COUNT
   35    FORMAT (1X,I7,10X,I7,10X,I7)
         N = N + 1
         READ (15,*) ID
         GO TO 15
      ENDIF
      PRINT*
      PRINT 40, N
   40 FORMAT (1X,I3,' GRIDS ANALYZED')
*
      END
*-----------------------------------------------------------*


17. *-----------------------------------------------------------*
      PROGRAM  NAVIG
*
```

```
      * This program reads the elevation data for a set of land
      * grids and determines the number of peaks in each grid.
      *
            INTEGER  MAP(100,100), I, J, ID, NROWS, NCOLS, COUNT
      *
            PRINT 5
        5 FORMAT (1X,'SUMMARY OF LAND GRID ANALYSIS')
      *
            OPEN (UNIT=15,FILE='ELEVTN',STATUS='OLD')
            READ (15,*) ID
       15 IF (ID.NE.99999) THEN
            READ (15,*) NROWS, NCOLS
            DO 20 I=1,NROWS
               READ (15,*) (MAP(I,J), J=1,NCOLS)
       20     CONTINUE
            COUNT = 0
            DO 30 I=2,NROWS-1
               DO 25 J=2,NCOLS-1
                  IF ((MAP(I-1,J).LT.MAP(I,J)).AND.
          +           (MAP(I+1,J).LT.MAP(I,J)).AND.
          +           (MAP(I,J-1).LT.MAP(I,J)).AND.
          +           (MAP(I,J+1).LT.MAP(I,J))) THEN
                       COUNT = COUNT + 1
                       PRINT 22, I, J
       22              FORMAT (1X,'PEAK AT LOCATION: ',I3,',',I3)
                  ENDIF
       25       CONTINUE
       30     CONTINUE
            PRINT 32
       32   FORMAT (1X,'IDENTIFICAITION  NUMBER OF POINTS    ',
          +            'NUMBER OF PEAKS')
            PRINT 35, ID, NROWS*NCOLS, COUNT
       35   FORMAT (1X,I7,10X,I7,10X,I7)
            READ (15,*) ID
            GO TO 15
          ENDIF
      *
            END
*--------------------------------------------------------------*

18. *--------------------------------------------------------------*
            PROGRAM  NAVIG
      *
      * This program reads the elevation data for a set of land
      * grids and determines the number of peaks in each grid.
      *
            INTEGER  MAP(100,100), I, J, ID, NROWS, NCOLS, COUNT
            REAL  PERC
      *
            PRINT 5
        5 FORMAT (1X,'SUMMARY OF LAND GRID ANALYSIS')
      *
            OPEN (UNIT=15,FILE='ELEVTN',STATUS='OLD')
            READ (15,*) ID
       15 IF (ID.NE.99999) THEN
```

150

```
            READ (15,*) NROWS, NCOLS
            DO 20 I=1,NROWS
               READ (15,*) (MAP(I,J), J=1,NCOLS)
   20       CONTINUE
            COUNT = 0
            DO 30 I=2,NROWS-1
               DO 25 J=2,NCOLS-1
                  IF ((MAP(I-1,J).LT.MAP(I,J)).AND.
     +               (MAP(I+1,J).LT.MAP(I,J)).AND.
     +               (MAP(I,J-1).LT.MAP(I,J)).AND.
     +               (MAP(I,J+1).LT.MAP(I,J))) THEN
                       COUNT = COUNT + 1
                       PRINT 22, I, J
   22                  FORMAT (1X,'PEAK AT LOCATION: ',I3,',',I3)
               ENDIF
   25       CONTINUE
   30       CONTINUE
            PRINT 32
   32       FORMAT (1X,'IDENTIFICAITION  NUMBER OF POINTS    ',
     +             'NUMBER OF PEAKS')
            PRINT 35, ID, NROWS*NCOLS, COUNT
   35       FORMAT (1X,I7,10X,I7,10X,I7)
            PERC = REAL(COUNT)/REAL(NROWS*NCOLS)*100.0
            PRINT 40, PERC
   40       FORMAT (1X,'PERCENT OF POINTS THAT ARE PEAKS = ',
     +             F5.1)
            READ (15,*) ID
            GO TO 15
         ENDIF
*
         END
*------------------------------------------------------------*
```

19. Solution in text.

20.
```
*------------------------------------------------------------*
      PROGRAM  NAVIG
*
*  This program reads the elevation data for a set of land
*  grids and determines the number of peaks in each grid.
*
      INTEGER  MAP(100,100), I, J, ID, NROWS, NCOLS,
     +         COUNT, SUM
*
      PRINT 5
    5 FORMAT (1X,'SUMMARY OF LAND GRID ANALYSIS')
      PRINT 10
   10 FORMAT (1X,'IDENTIFICATION   NUMBER OF POINTS    ',
     +        'NUMBER OF PEAKS')
*
      OPEN (UNIT=15,FILE='ELEVTN',STATUS='OLD')
      READ (15,*) ID
   15 IF (ID.NE.99999) THEN
         READ (15,*) NROWS, NCOLS
         DO 20 I=1,NROWS
```

```
                    READ (15,*) (MAP(I,J), J=1,NCOLS)
      20      CONTINUE
              COUNT = 0
              DO 30 I=2,NROWS-1
                  DO 25 J=2,NCOLS-1
                      IF ((MAP(I-1,J).LT.MAP(I,J)).AND.
     +                    (MAP(I+1,J).LT.MAP(I,J)).AND.
     +                    (MAP(I,J-1).LT.MAP(I,J)).AND.
     +                    (MAP(I,J+1).LT.MAP(I,J))) THEN
                          COUNT = COUNT + 1
                      ENDIF
      25          CONTINUE
      30      CONTINUE
              PRINT 35, ID, NROWS*NCOLS, COUNT
      35      FORMAT (1X,I7,10X,I7,10X,I7)
              SUM = 0
              DO 45 I=1,NROWS
                  DO 40 J=1,NCOLS
                      SUM = SUM + MAP(I,J)
      40          CONTINUE
      45      CONTINUE
              PRINT 50, REAL(SUM)/REAL(NROWS*NCOLS)
      50      FORMAT (1X,'AVERAGE ELEVATION = ',F6.2)
              READ (15,*) ID
              GO TO 15
          ENDIF
   *
          END
   *-------------------------------------------------------------*

  21.       INTEGER  K(50), MAX, I
            .
            .
            .
            MAX = K(I)
            DO 10 I=2,50
                IF (K(I).GT.MAX) MAX = K(I)
         10 CONTINUE
            PRINT 15, MAX
         15 FORMAT (1X,'MAXIMUM VALUE IS ',I5)

  22.       INTEGER K(50), I, MININ, LOCATE
            .
            .
            .
            MININ = 999999
            DO 5 I = 1,50
                IF (K(I).LT.MININ) MININ = K(I)
          5 CONTINUE
            DO 10 I = 1,50
                IF (K(I).EQ.MININ) PRINT 15, I, MININ
         10 CONTINUE
         10 FORMAT (1X,10X,'MINIMUM VALUE OF K IS',/,1X,10,'K(',I2,
     +          ') = ',I5)
```

```
23.         INTEGER  K(50), NP, NZ, NN, I
            DATA  NP, NZ, NN /3*0/
               .
               .
               .
            DO 20 I=1,50
               IF (K(I).GT.0) THEN
                  NP = NP + 1
               ELSEIF (K(I).EQ.0) THEN
                  NZ = NZ + 1
               ELSE
                  NN = NN + 1
               END
         20 CONTINUE
            PRINT 25, NP
         25 FORMAT (1X,I3,' POSITIVE VALUES')
            PRINT 30, NZ
         30 FORMAT (1X,I3,' ZERO VALUES')
            PRINT 35, NN
         35 FORMAT (1X,I3,' NEGATIVE VALUES')

24.         INTEGER  K(50)
               .
               .
               .
            DO 5 I = 1,50
               K(I) = ABS(K(I))
          5 CONTINUE
            DO 10 I = 1,49,2
               PRINT 10, K(I), K(I+1)
         10 CONTINUE
```

25. Solution in text.

```
26.         INTEGER  WIND(10,7), I, J
               .
               .
               .
            PRINT*, '    CHICAGO WIND VELOCITY (MILES/HOUR)'
            PRINT*
            DO 5 I = 1,10
               PRINT 10, (WIND(I,J), J = 1,7)
          5 CONTINUE
         10 FORMAT (1X,7(I3,3X))

27.         DO 75 K=N-9,N
               PRINT 70, K, M(K)
         70    FORMAT (1X,'M(',I3,') = ',F5.1)
            CONTINUE

28.         INTEGER  NUM(100), I, TEMP
               .
               .
               .
            DO 5 I = 1,50
```

```
                    TEMP = NUM(101-I)
                    NUM(101-I) = NUM(I)
                    NUM(I) = TEMP
              5 CONTINUE

29.           INTEGER  TEST(100), SUM1, SUM2, I
                    .
                    .
                    .
              SUM1 = 0
              SUM2 = 0
              DO 10 I=1,100
                 IF (I.LE.50) THEN
                    SUM1 = SUM1 + TEST(I)
                 ELSE
                    SUM2 = SUM2 + TEST(I)
                 ENDIF
          10 CONTINUE
             PRINT 20, REAL(SUM1)/50.0, REAL(SUM2)/50.0
          20 FORMAT (1X,'10X,'AVERAGES'/
             +          1X,'1ST 50 EXAMS',4X,'2ND 50 EXAMS'/
             +          1X,2X,F6.2,10X,F6.2)

30.   *-----------------------------------------------------------*
          PROGRAM SWITCH
      *
      * This program reads in values and then reverses their order.
      *
          INTEGER  NUM(20), I, J
      *
          OPEN (UNIT=1,FILE='NUMBER',STATUS='OLD')
      *
          I = 1
          READ (1,*) NUM(I)
        5 IF (NUM(I).NE.9999) THEN
             I = I + 1
             READ (1,*) NUM(I)
             GO TO 5
          ENDIF
      *
          PRINT*,'VALUES IN REVERSE ORDER'
          DO 10 J = I,1,-1
             PRINT 8, NUM(J)
        8     FORMAT (1X,I8)
       10 CONTINUE
      *
          END
      *-----------------------------------------------------------*

31.   *-----------------------------------------------------------*
          PROGRAM ADJUST
      *
      * This program reads in an array and smoothes
      * the values by averaging.
      *
```

154

```
      INTEGER  I
      REAL  Y(20), Z(20)
*
      OPEN (UNIT=1,FILE='EXPR',STATUS='OLD')
*
      DO 5 I = 1,20
         READ (1,*) Y(I)
    5 CONTINUE
*
      Z(1) = Y(1)
      Z(20) = Y(20)
*
      DO 10 I = 2,19
         Z(I) = (Y(I-1) + Y(I) + Y(I+1))/3.0
   10 CONTINUE
*
      PRINT*, 'ORIGINAL & SMOOTHED VALUES'
      DO 15 I = 1,20
         PRINT 12, Y(I), Z(I)
   12    FORMAT (1X,F8.3,5X,F8.3)
   15 CONTINUE
*
      END
*------------------------------------------------------------*

32. *------------------------------------------------------------*
      PROGRAM LIFE
*
*  This program computes the commission of 12 salespeople
*  according to their sales percentage.
*
      INTEGER  IDSALE(12,2), I, TOTSAL
      REAL  PERCNT, TOTCOM, COMM, TPERCN
      DATA  TOTSAL, TOTCOM, TPERCN /0,2*0.0/
*
      OPEN (UNIT=1,FILE='SALES',STATUS='OLD')
*
      DO 5 I = 1,12
         READ (1,*) IDSALE(I,1), IDSALE(I,2)
         TOTSAL = TOTSAL + IDSALE(I,2)
    5 CONTINUE
*
      PRINT*, '       MONTHLY COMMISSION REPORT'
      PRINT*, ' ID      SALES      PERCENT      COMMISSION'
*
      DO 15 I = 1,12
         PERCNT = REAL(IDSALE(I,2))/REAL(TOTSAL)*100.0
         TPERCN = TPERCN + PERCNT
         IF (PERCNT.LT.25.0) THEN
            COMM = 0.02*REAL(IDSALE(I,2))
         ELSEIF (PERCNT.LT.75.0) THEN
            COMM = 0.04*REAL(IDSALE(I,2))
         ELSE
            COMM = 0.06*REAL(IDSALE(I,2))
         ENDIF
```

```
                TOTCOM = TOTCOM + COMM
                PRINT 10, IDSALE(I,1), IDSALE(I,2), PERCNT, COMM
      10      FORMAT (1X,2X,I3,4X,'$ ',I5,'.',6X,F6.2,5X,'$ ',F8.2)
          15 CONTINUE
      *
                PRINT 20, TOTSAL, TPERCN, TOTCOM
          20 FORMAT (1X,'TOTALS    $',I6,'.',6X,F6.2,5X,'$',F9.2)
      *
                END
      *----------------------------------------------------------*


33.   *----------------------------------------------------------*
                PROGRAM RAINS
      *
      * This program calculates yearly rainfall averages
      * from a file called 'WATER'.
      *
                INTEGER  I, J, MAXMON, MINMON, MAXYEA, MINYEA
                REAL  RAIN(12,5), MAXRAI, MINRAI, AVERAI
      *
                OPEN (UNIT=1,FILE='WATER',STATUS='OLD')
                READ (1,*) ((RAIN(I,J), J = 1,5), I = 1,12)
      *
                MAXRAI = 0.0
                MINRAI = 999.0
      *
                PRINT*, '     AVERAGE YEARLY RAINFALL'
                DO 15 I = 1978,1982
                   AVERAI = 0.0
                   DO 5 J = 1,12
                      AVERAI = AVERAI + RAIN(J,I-1977)
                      IF (RAIN(J,I-1977).GT.MAXRAI) THEN
                         MAXRAI = RAIN(J,I-1977)
                         MAXMON = J
                         MAXYEA = I
                      ENDIF
                      IF (RAIN(J,I-1977).LT.MINRAI) THEN
                         MINRAI = RAIN(J,I-1977)
                         MINMON = J
                         MINYEA = I
                      ENDIF
           5      CONTINUE
                   PRINT 10, I, AVERAI
          10      FORMAT (1X,5X,I4,' - ',F6.2)
          15 CONTINUE
      *
                PRINT 20, MAXMON, MAXYEA, MINMON, MINYEA
          20 FORMAT (/,1X,5X,'MAXIMUM RAINFALL',/,1X,5X,'MONTH ',I2,
               +       ' YEAR ',I4,//,1X,5X,'MINIMUM RAINFALL',/,1X,5X,
               +       'MONTH ',I2,'  YEAR ',I4)
                END
      *----------------------------------------------------------*


34.   *----------------------------------------------------------*
                PROGRAM PLANE
```

```
*
* This program finds two open adjacent seats
* in a reservation list.
*
      INTEGER  SEAT(38,6), COUNT, I, J
*
      OPEN (UNIT=1,FILE='FLIGHT',STATUS='OLD')
      READ (1,*) ((SEAT(I,J), J = 1,6), I = 1,38)
*
      COUNT = 0
      PRINT*, '    AVAILABLE SEAT PAIRS'
      PRINT*, '       ROW    SEATS'
*
      DO 15 I = 1,38
         DO 10 J = 1,5
            IF ((SEAT(I,J)+SEAT(I,J+1).EQ.0).AND.(J.NE.3)) THEN
               COUNT = COUNT + 1
               PRINT 5, I,J,J + 1
 5             FORMAT (1X,9X,I2,6X,I1,',',I1)
            ENDIF
 10      CONTINUE
 15   CONTINUE
*
      IF (COUNT.EQ.0) THEN
         PRINT*, '  NO SEAT PAIRS AVAILABLE'
      ENDIF
      END
*------------------------------------------------------------*

35.   *------------------------------------------------------------*
      PROGRAM BUYERS
*
* This program calculates the least
* shipping cost for a buyer.
*
      INTEGER  I, J
      REAL   COST(5,6), ORDER(5,6), TOTCOS, TOTIND(6)
      DATA TOTCOS, TOTIND /7*0.0/
*
      OPEN (UNIT=1,FILE='SHIPPING',STATUS='OLD')
      OPEN (UNIT=2,FILE='PURCHASE',STATUS='OLD')
      READ (1,*) ((COST(I,J), J = 1,6), I = 1,5)
      READ (2,*) ((ORDER(I,J), J = 1,6), I = 1,5)
*
      PRINT 5
 5    FORMAT (1X,34X,'BUYER',//,1X,16X,'1',7X,'2',7X,'3',
     +        7X,'4',7X,'5',7X,'6')
      PRINT 10, (I, (COST(I,J), J = 1,6), I = 1,5)
 10   FORMAT (5(1X,12X,49('-'),/,1X,'WAREHOUSE ',I1,' |',
     +        6('$',F6.2,'|'),/),13X,49('-'))
*
      PRINT 15
 15   FORMAT (//,1X,'PURCHASE ORDER',/)
*
      DO 30 J = 1,6
```

```
                 DO 20 I = 1,5
                    TOTIND(J) = TOTIND(J) + COST(I,J)*ORDER(I,J)
         20      CONTINUE
                 TOTCOS = TOTCOS + TOTIND(J)
                 PRINT 25, J, TOTIND(J)
         25      FORMAT (1X,'SHIPPING COST TO BUYER ',I1,' = ',F8.2)
         30 CONTINUE
      *
             PRINT 35, TOTCOS
         35 FORMAT (/,1X,'TOTAL SHIPPING COST',6X,'$',F9.2)
      *
             END
      *------------------------------------------------------------*

36.   *------------------------------------------------------------*
             PROGRAM CONVRT
      *
      *  This program converts a Gregorian date to a Julian date.
      *
             INTEGER  DAY, YEAR, JULIAN, MONTH(12), MON, I, NUMDAY,
            +         INPUT
             DATA  MONTH /31,28,31,30,31,30,31,31,30,31,30,31/
      *
             PRINT*, 'ENTER MONTH, DAY, YEAR (ONLY LAST TWO DIGITS)'
             READ*, INPUT
      *
             MON = INT(INPUT/10000)
             DAY = INT((INPUT-MON*10000)/100)
             YEAR = INT((INPUT-MON*10000-DAY*100))
             YEAR = 1900 + YEAR
             NUMDAY = 0
      *
             DO 5 I = 1,MON-1
                NUMDAY = NUMDAY + MONTH(I)
          5 CONTINUE
             NUMDAY = NUMDAY + DAY
      *
             IF (MOD(YEAR,100).EQ.0) THEN
                IF (MOD(YEAR,400).EQ.0) THEN
                   NUMDAY = NUMDAY + 1
                ENDIF
             ELSE
                IF (MOD(YEAR,4).EQ.0) THEN
                   NUMDAY = NUMDAY + 1
                ENDIF
             ENDIF
      *
             YEAR = YEAR - 1900
             JULIAN = YEAR*1000 + NUMDAY
      *
             PRINT 5, MON, DAY, YEAR
          5 FORMAT (1X,'GREGORIAN DATE ',3I2)
             PRINT 6, JULIAN
          6 FORMAT (1X,'CONVERTS TO JULIAN DATE',I5)
      *
```

```
      END
--------------------------------------------------------------*

37.   *--------------------------------------------------------------*
      PROGRAM CONVRT
*
*  This program converts a Julain date to a Gregorian date.
*
      INTEGER  DAY, YEAR, JULIAN, MONTH(12), MON, I
      DATA  MONTH /31,28,31,30,31,30,31,31,30,31,30,31/
*
      PRINT*, 'ENTER JULIAN DATE'
      READ*, JULIAN
*
      YEAR = INT(JULIAN/1000)
      DAY = INT(JULIAN - YEAR*1000)
      YEAR = YEAR + 1900
*
      IF (MOD(YEAR,100).EQ.0) THEN
         IF (MOD(YEAR,400).EQ.0) THEN
            MONTH(2) = 29
         ENDIF
      ELSE
         IF (MOD(YEAR,4).EQ.O) THEN
            MONTH(2) = 29
         ENDIF
      ENDIF
*
      I = 1
      YEAR = YEAR - 1900
      MON = 1
    5 IF (DAY.GT.MONTH(I)) THEN
         MON = MON + 1
         DAY = DAY - MONTH(I)
         I = I + 1
         GO TO 5
      ENDIF
*
      PRINT 9, JULIAN
    9 FORMAT (1X,'JULIAN DATE ',I5)
      PRINT 10, MON, DAY, YEAR
   10 FORMAT (1X,'CONVERTS TO GREGORIAN DATE  ',
     +        I2,'/',I2,'/',I2)
*
      END
      *--------------------------------------------------------------*

38.   *--------------------------------------------------------------*
      PROGRAM  PHONE
*
*  This program eliminates redundant numbers from a phone file.
*
      INTEGER  NUMBER(500), I, J, TEMP
*
      OPEN (UNIT=1,FILE='DIAL',STATUS='OLD')
```

```
*
      I = 0
      READ (1,*) NUMBER(I+1)
    5 IF (NUMBER(I+1).NE.9999999) THEN
         I = I + 1
         READ (1,*) NUMBER(I+1)
         GO TO 5
      ENDIF
*
      TEMP = I
      DO 15 I = 1,TEMP
         DO 10 J = I+1,TEMP
            IF (NUMBER(I).EQ.NUMBER(J)) THEN
               NUMBER(J) = 9999999
            ENDIF
   10    CONTINUE
   15 CONTINUE
*
      PRINT*, '  NUMBERS DIALED'
      DO 25 I = 1, TEMP
         IF (NUMBER(I).NE.9999999) THEN
            PRINT 20, NUMBER(I)
   20       FORMAT (1X,5X,I7)
         ENDIF
   25 CONTINUE
*
      END
*-----------------------------------------------------------*
```

1. *--*

```
      PROGRAM  TABLE1
*
*  This program generates a temperature conversion table.
*
      INTEGER  UNITS, COUNT, NUM
      REAL  CENT, FAHREN, FIRST, CHANGE, NEXT,
     +      NEW, TEMP
      CENT(TEMP) = (TEMP - 32.0)*0.5555556
      FAHREN(TEMP) = 1.8*TEMP + 32.0
*
      PRINT*, 'ENTER 1 TO CONVERT FAHRENHEIT TO CENTIGRADE'
      PRINT*, 'ENTER 2 TO CONVERT CENTIGRADE TO FAHRENHEIT: '
      READ*, UNITS
      PRINT*, 'ENTER NUMBER OF DEGREES FOR FIRST LINE'
      READ*, FIRST
      PRINT*, 'ENTER CHANGE IN DEGREES BETWEEN LINES'
      READ*, CHANGE
      PRINT*, 'ENTER NUMBER OF LINES FOR TABLE'
      READ*, NUM
*
      PRINT 5
    5 FORMAT (1X,10X,'TEMPERATURE CONVERSION TABLE')
      IF (UNITS.EQ.1) THEN
         PRINT 10
   10    FORMAT (1X,'DEGREES, FAHRENHEIT',6X,
     +           'DEGREES, CENTIGRADE')
      ELSE
         PRINT 15
   15    FORMAT (1X,'DEGREES, CENTIGRADE',6X,
     +           'DEGREES, FAHRENHEIT')
      ENDIF
      NEXT = FIRST
      COUNT = 0
   20 IF (COUNT.LT.NUM) THEN
         IF (UNITS.EQ.1) THEN
            NEW = CENT(NEXT)
         ELSE
            NEW = FAHREN(NEXT)
         ENDIF
         PRINT 25, NEXT, NEW
   25    FORMAT (1X,F9.2,18X,F9.2)
         NEXT = NEXT + CHANGE
         COUNT = COUNT + 1
         GO TO 20
      ENDIF
*
      END
```

--

2. *--*

```
      PROGRAM  TABLE1
*
```

```
*   This program generates a temperature conversion table.
*
      INTEGER  UNITS
      REAL  CENT, KELVIN, FIRST, CHANGE, NEXT, LAST,
     +      NEW, TEMP
      CENT(TEMP) = TEMP - 273.15
      KELVIN(TEMP) = TEMP + 273.15
*
      PRINT*, 'ENTER 1 TO CONVERT KELVIN TO CENTIGRADE'
      PRINT*, 'ENTER 2 TO CONVERT CENTIGRADE TO KELVIN: '
      READ*, UNITS
      PRINT*, 'ENTER NUMBER OF DEGREES FOR FIRST LINE'
      READ*, FIRST
      PRINT*, 'ENTER CHANGE IN DEGREES BETWEEN LINES'
      READ*, CHANGE
      PRINT*, 'ENTER NUMBER OF DEGREES FOR LAST LINE'
      READ*, LAST
*
      PRINT 5
    5 FORMAT (1X,10X,'TEMPERATURE CONVERSION TABLE')
      IF (UNITS.EQ.1) THEN
         PRINT 10
   10    FORMAT (1X,'DEGREES, KELVIN',6X,
     +           'DEGREES, CENTIGRADE')
      ELSE
         PRINT 15
   15    FORMAT (1X,'DEGREES, CENTIGRADE',6X,
     +           'DEGREES, KELVIN')
      ENDIF
      NEXT = FIRST
   20 IF (NEXT.LE.LAST) THEN
         IF (UNITS.EQ.1) THEN
            NEW = CENT(NEXT)
         ELSE
            NEW = KELVIN(NEXT)
         ENDIF
         PRINT 25, NEXT, NEW
   25    FORMAT (1X,F9.2,18X,F9.2)
         NEXT = NEXT + CHANGE
         GO TO 20
      ENDIF
*
      END
*-------------------------------------------------------------*


3.    *-------------------------------------------------------------*
      PROGRAM  TABLE1
*
*   This program generates a temperature conversion table.
*
      INTEGER  UNITS
      REAL  RANKIN, FAHREN, FIRST, CHANGE, LAST, NEXT,
     +      NEW, TEMP
      RANKIN(TEMP) = TEMP + 459.67
      FAHREN(TEMP) = TEMP - 459.67
```

```
*
          PRINT*, 'ENTER 1 TO CONVERT FAHRENHEIT TO RANKIN'
          PRINT*, 'ENTER 2 TO CONVERT RANKIN TO FAHRENHEIT: '
          READ*, UNITS
          PRINT*, 'ENTER NUMBER OF DEGREES FOR FIRST LINE: '
          READ*, FIRST
          PRINT*, 'ENTER CHANGE IN DEGREES BETWEEN LINES: '
          READ*, CHANGE
          PRINT*, 'ENTER NUMBER OF DEGREES FOR LAST LINE: '
          READ*, LAST
*
          PRINT 5
        5 FORMAT (1X,10X,'TEMPERATURE CONVERSION TABLE')
          IF (UNITS.EQ.1) THEN
              PRINT 10
       10     FORMAT (1X,'DEGREES, FAHRENHEIT',6X,
          +            'DEGREES, RANKIN')
          ELSE
              PRINT 15
       15     FORMAT (1X,'DEGREES, RANKIN',6X,
          +            'DEGREES, FAHRENHEIT')
          ENDIF
          NEXT = FIRST
       20 IF (NEXT.LE.LAST) THEN
              IF (UNITS.EQ.1) THEN
                  NEW = RANKIN(NEXT)
              ELSE
                  NEW = FAHREN(NEXT)
              ENDIF
              PRINT 25, NEXT, NEW
       25     FORMAT (1X,F9.2,18X,F9.2)
              NEXT = NEXT + CHANGE
              GO TO 20
          ENDIF
*
          END
*-------------------------------------------------------------*


4.  *-------------------------------------------------------------*
          PROGRAM  TABLE1
*
*   This program generates a temperature conversion table.
*
          INTEGER  UNITS
          REAL  RANKIN, KELVIN, FIRST, CHANGE, NEXT, LAST,
          +       NEW, TEMP
          RANKIN(TEMP) = 1.8*TEMP
          KELVIN(TEMP) = TEMP/1.8
*
          PRINT*, 'ENTER 1 TO CONVERT KELVIN TO RANKIN'
          PRINT*, 'ENTER 2 TO CONVERT RANKIN TO KELVIN: '
          READ*, UNITS
          PRINT*, 'ENTER NUMBER OF DEGREES FOR FIRST LINE'
          READ*, FIRST
          PRINT*, 'ENTER CHANGE IN DEGREES BETWEEN LINES'
```

```
          READ*, CHANGE
          PRINT*, 'ENTER NUMBER OF DEGREES FOR LAST LINE'
          READ*, LAST
   *
          PRINT 5
        5 FORMAT (1X,10X,'TEMPERATURE CONVERSION TABLE')
          IF (UNITS.EQ.1) THEN
             PRINT 10
       10    FORMAT (1X,'DEGREES, KELVIN',6X,
          +             'DEGREES, RANKIN')
          ELSE
             PRINT 15
       15    FORMAT (1X,'DEGREES, RANKIN',6X,
          +             'DEGREES, KELVIN')
          ENDIF
          NEXT = FIRST
       20 IF (NEXT.LE.LAST) THEN
             IF (UNITS.EQ.1) THEN
                NEW = RANKIN(NEXT)
             ELSE
                NEW = KELVIN(NEXT)
             ENDIF
             PRINT 25, NEXT, NEW
       25    FORMAT (1X,F9.2,18X,F9.2)
             NEXT = NEXT + CHANGE
             GO TO 20
          ENDIF
   *
          END
   *------------------------------------------------------------*
```

5. Solution in text.

6.
```
   *------------------------------------------------------------*
          PROGRAM   REPORT
   *
   *  This program generates a report from the daily
   *  production information for a set of oil wells.
   *
          INTEGER  MO, DA, YR, ID, N, I
          REAL  OIL(7), TOTAL, AVE, INDAVE
          CHARACTER*8 DATE
          DATA  N, TOTAL /0, 0.0/
   *
          OPEN (UNIT=12,FILE='WELLS',STATUS='OLD')
          READ (12,*) MO, DA, YR
          PRINT*, 'ENTER CURRENT DATE IN THE FORM XX-XX-XX'
          READ 1, DATE
        1 FORMAT(A)
          PRINT 2, DATE
        2 FORMAT(1X,63X,A)
          PRINT*, 'OIL WELL PRODUCTION'
          PRINT 5, MO, DA, YR
        5 FORMAT (1X,'WEEK OF ',I2,'-',I2,'-',I2)
          PRINT*
```

```
      PRINT*, 'WELL ID        AVERAGE PRODUCTION'
      PRINT*, '                 (IN BARRELS)'
*
      READ (12,*) ID, (OIL(I), I=1,7)
   10 IF (ID.NE.99999) THEN
         INDAVE = AVE(OIL,7)
         PRINT 15, ID, INDAVE
   15    FORMAT (1X,I5,9X,F6.2)
         N = N + 1
         TOTAL = TOTAL + INDAVE
         READ (12,*) ID, (OIL(I), I=1,7)
         GO TO 10
      ENDIF
*
      PRINT*
      PRINT 20, N, TOTAL/REAL(N)
   20 FORMAT (1X,'OVERALL AVERAGE FOR ',I3,
     +          ' WELLS IS ',F6.2)
*
      END
*------------------------------------------------------------*
      (no changes in function AVE)
*------------------------------------------------------------*
```

7. Solution in text.

8.
```
*------------------------------------------------------------*
      PROGRAM  REPORT
*
*  This program generates a report from the daily
*  production information for a set of oil wells.
*
      INTEGER  MO, DA, YR, ID, N, I
      REAL  OIL(7), TOTAL, AVE, INDAVE, MAX
      DATA  N, TOTAL /0, 0.0/
*
      OPEN (UNIT=12,FILE='WELLS',STATUS='OLD')
      READ (12,*) MO, DA, YR
      PRINT*, 'OIL WELL PRODUCTION'
      PRINT 5, MO, DA, YR
    5 FORMAT (1X,'WEEK OF ',I2,'-',I2,'-',I2)
      PRINT*
      PRINT*, 'WELL ID        AVERAGE PRODUCTION        ',
     +        'MAXIMUM DAILY'
      PRINT*, '                 (IN BARRELS)           ',
     +        'PRODUCTION (BARRELS)'
*
      READ (12,*) ID, (OIL(I), I=1,7)
   10 IF (ID.NE.99999) THEN
         INDAVE = AVE(OIL,7)
         DAYMAX = MAX(OIL,7)
         PRINT 15, ID, INDAVE, DAYMAX
   15    FORMAT (1X,I5,12X,F6.2,20X,F6.2)
         N = N + 1
         TOTAL = TOTAL + INDAVE
```

165

```
                   READ (12,*) ID, (OIL(I), I=1,7)
                   GO TO 10
             ENDIF
*

      PRINT*
      PRINT 20, N, TOTAL/REAL(N)
   20 FORMAT (1X,'OVERALL AVERAGE FOR ',I3,
     +          ' WELLS IS ',F6.2)
*

      END
*-------------------------------------------------------------*
      REAL FUNCTION  MAX(X,N)
*
*  THIS FUNCTION DETERMINES THE MAXIMUM
*  OF A REAL ARRAY WITH N VALUES
*
      INTEGER N, I
      REAL X(N)
*
      MAX = X(1)
      DO 10 I = 2, N
         IF  (X(I).GT.MAX)  MAX = X(I)
   10    CONTINUE
*
      RETURN
      END
*-------------------------------------------------------------*
      (no changes in function AVE)
*-------------------------------------------------------------*
```

9.
```
*-------------------------------------------------------------*
      PROGRAM  REPORT
*
*  The program generates a report from the daily
*  production information for a set of oil wells.
*
      INTEGER  MO, DA, YR, ID, N, I
      REAL  OIL(7), TOTAL, AVE, INDAVE, INDTOT, SUM
      DATA  N, TOTAL /0, 0.0/
*
      OPEN (UNIT=12,FILE='WELLS',STATUS='OLD')
      READ (12,*) MO, DA, YR
      PRINT*, 'OIL WELL PRODUCTION'
      PRINT 5, MO, DA, YR
    5 FORMAT (1X,'WEEK OF ',I2,'-',I2,'-',I2)
      PRINT*
      PRINT*, 'WELL ID       AVERAGE PRODUCTION    TOTAL',
     +        ' PRODUCTION'
      PRINT*, '                 (IN BARRELS)         (IN BARRELS)'
*
      READ (12,*) ID, (OIL(I), I=1,7)
   10 IF (ID.NE.99999) THEN
         INDAVE = AVE(OIL,7)
         INDTOT = SUM(OIL,7)
         PRINT 15, ID, INDAVE, INDTOT
```

```
15      FORMAT (1X,I5,12X,F6.2,17X,F6.2)
        N = N + 1
        TOTAL = TOTAL + INDAVE
        READ (12,*) ID, (OIL(I), I=1,7)
        GO TO 10
     ENDIF
*
     PRINT*
     PRINT 20, N, TOTAL/REAL(N)
  20 FORMAT (1X,'OVERALL AVERAGE FOR ',I3,
     +          ' WELLS IS ',F6.2)
*
     END
*-------------------------------------------------------------*
*
     REAL FUNCTION  AVE(X,N)
*
* This function computes the average
* of a real array with N values.
*
     INTEGER  N
     REAL  X(N), SUM
*
     AVE = SUM(X,N)/REAL(N)
*
     RETURN
     END
*-------------------------------------------------------------*
*
     REAL FUNCTION  SUM(X,N)
*
* This function computes the sum
* of a real array with N values.
*
     INTEGER  N,I
     REAL  X(N), SUM
*
     SUM = 0.0
     DO 10 I=1,N
         SUM = SUM + X(I)
  10 CONTINUE
*
     RETURN
     END
*-------------------------------------------------------------*


10.  *-------------------------------------------------------------*
     PROGRAM  REPORT
*
* This program generates a report from the daily
* production information for a set of oil wells.
*
     INTEGER  MO, DA, YR, ID, N, I
     REAL  OIL(7), TOTAL, AVE, INDAVE
     DATA  N, TOTAL /0, 0.0/
```

167

```
*
      OPEN (UNIT=12,FILE='WELLS',STATUS='OLD')
      READ (12,*) MO, DA, YR
      PRINT*, 'OIL WELL PRODUCTION'
      PRINT 5, MO, DA, YR
    5 FORMAT (1X,'WEEK OF ',I2,'-',I2,'-',I2)
      PRINT*
      PRINT*, 'WELL ID        AVERAGE PRODUCTION'
      PRINT*, '                  (IN BARRELS)'
*
      READ (12,*) ID, (OIL(I), I=1,7)
   10 IF (ID.NE.99999) THEN
         INDAVE = AVE(OIL,7)
         PRINT 15, ID, INDAVE
   15    FORMAT (1X,I5,9X,F6.2)
         N = N + 1
         TOTAL = TOTAL + INDAVE
         READ (12,*) ID, (OIL(I), I=1,7)
         GO TO 10
      ENDIF
*
      PRINT*
      PRINT 20, N, TOTAL/REAL(N)
   20 FORMAT (1X,'OVERALL AVERAGE FOR ',I3,
     +          ' WELLS IS ',F6.2)
*
      END
*------------------------------------------------------------*
      REAL FUNCTION  AVE(X,N)
*
*  THIS FUNCTION COMPUTES THE AVERAGE OF
*  NON-ZERO VALUES IN A REAL ARRAY WITH N VALUES
*
      INTEGER  N, I, COUNT
      REAL  X(N), SUM
*
      SUM = 0.0
      COUNT = 0
      DO 10 I=1,N
         IF  (X(I).NE.0)  THEN
            SUM = SUM + X(I)
            COUNT = COUNT + 1
         ENDIF
   10 CONTINUE
      AVE = SUM/REAL(COUNT)
*
      RETURN
      END
*------------------------------------------------------------*


11. *------------------------------------------------------------*
      PROGRAM  ANALYZ
*
*  This program reads traffic flow informaton from a
*  data file and computes the average number of cars
```

168

```
*   per minute through a specific intersection.
*
       INTEGER  ID, FILEID, BEGIN, END, FLOW,
      +          MINUTE, TOTMIN, TOTCAR
       DATA  TOTMIN, TOTCAR /0, 0/
*
       PRINT*, 'ENTER INTERSECTION IDENTIFICATION: '
       READ*, ID
       OPEN (UNIT=10,FILE='CARS',STATUS='OLD')
     5 READ (10,*,END=50) FILEID, BEGIN, END, FLOW
          IF (FILEID.EQ.ID) THEN
             TOTMIN = TOTMIN + MINUTE(BEGIN,END)
             TOTCAR = TOTCAR + FLOW
          ENDIF
          GO TO 5
    50 IF (TOTMIN.EQ.0) THEN
          PRINT 55, ID
    55    FORMAT (1X,'NO OBSERVATIONS FOR INTERSECTION ',I3)
       ELSE
          PRINT 60, ID
    60    FORMAT (1X,'INTERSECTION ',I3)
          PRINT 65, REAL(TOTCAR)/REAL(TOTMIN)
    65    FORMAT (1X,'AVERAGE CARS PER MINUTE = ',F5.2)
          PRINT 70, TOTCAR, TOTMIN
    70    FORMAT (1X,'TOTAL CARS: ',I5,2X,'TOTAL MINUTES: ',I5)
       ENDIF
*
       END
*-----------------------------------------------------------*
       (no changes in function MINUTE)
*-----------------------------------------------------------*

12. *-----------------------------------------------------------*
       PROGRAM  ANALYZ
*
*  This program reads traffic flow informaton from a
*  data file and computes the average number of cars
*  per minute through a specific intersection.
*
       INTEGER  ID, FILEID, BEGIN, END, FLOW,
      +          MINUTE, TOTMIN, TOTCAR, CARS, TIME
       DATA  TOTMIN, TOTCAR, CARS, TIME /0, 0, 0, 0/
*
       PRINT*, 'ENTER INTERSECTION IDENTIFICATION: '
       READ*, ID
       OPEN (UNIT=10,FILE='CARS',STATUS='OLD')
     5 READ (10,*,END=50) FILEID, BEGIN, END, FLOW
          TIME = TIME + MINUTE(BEGIN,END)
          CARS = CARS + FLOW
          IF (FILEID.EQ.ID) THEN
             TOTMIN = TOTMIN + MINUTE(BEGIN,END)
             TOTCAR = TOTCAR + FLOW
          ENDIF
          GO TO 5
    50 IF (TOTMIN.EQ.0) THEN
```

```
               PRINT 55, ID
      55       FORMAT (1X,'NO OBSERVATIONS FOR INTERSECTION ',I3)
            ELSE
               PRINT 60, ID
      60       FORMAT (1X,'INTERSECTION ',I3)
               PRINT 65, REAL(TOTCAR)/REAL(TOTMIN)
      65       FORMAT (1X,'AVERAGE CARS PER MINUTE = ',F5.2)
            ENDIF
            PRINT 70, REAL(CARS)/REAL(TIME)
      70 FORMAT (1X,'AVERAGE CARS PER MINUTE FOR ALL INTERSECTIONS = '
          +       F7.2)
   *
            END
   *------------------------------------------------------------*
            (no changes for function MINUTE)
   *------------------------------------------------------------*

13. *------------------------------------------------------------*
            PROGRAM   ANALYZ
   *
   * This program reads traffic flow information from a
   * data file and computes the average number of cars
   * per minute through a specific intersection.
   *
            INTEGER  ID, FILEID, BEGIN, END, FLOW,
          +          MINUTE, TOTMIN, TOTCAR
            DATA   TOTMIN, TOTCAR /0, 0/
   *
            PRINT*, 'ENTER INTERSECTION IDENTIFICATION: '
            READ*, ID
       1 IF (ID.NE.99999) THEN
            OPEN (UNIT=10,FILE='CARS',STATUS='OLD')
       5     READ (10,*,END=50) FILEID, BEGIN, END, FLOW
            IF (FILEID.EQ.ID) THEN
               TOTMIN = TOTMIN + MINUTE(BEGIN,END)
               TOTCAR = TOTCAR + FLOW
            ENDIF
            GO TO 5
      50    IF (TOTMIN.EQ.0) THEN
               PRINT 55, ID
      55       FORMAT (1X,'NO OBSERVATIONS FOR INTERSECTION ',I3)
            ELSE
               PRINT 60, ID
      60       FORMAT (1X,'INTERSECTION ',I3)
               PRINT 65, REAL(TOTCAR)/REAL(TOTMIN)
      65       FORMAT (1X,'AVERAGE CARS PER MINUTE = ',F5.2)
            ENDIF
            PRINT*, 'ENTER INTERSECTION IDENTIFICATION'
            READ*, ID
            TOTMIN = 0
            TOTCAR = 0
            CLOSE (UNIT=10)
            GO TO 1
         ENDIF
   *
```

```
      END
*------------------------------------------------------------*
      (no changes in function MINUTE)
*------------------------------------------------------------*

14.   *------------------------------------------------------------*
      PROGRAM  ANALYZ
*
*  This program reads traffic flow information from a
*  data file and computes the average number of cars
*  per minute through a specific intersection.
*
      INTEGER  ID, FILEID, BEGIN, END, FLOW, I,
     +          MINUTE, TOTMIN, TOTCAR, INTER(200)
      LOGICAL  COUNTD
      DATA  TOTMIN, TOTCAR, INTER(1) /0, 0, 99/
*
      PRINT*, 'ENTER INTERSECTION IDENTIFICATION'
      READ*, ID
      OPEN (UNIT=10,FILE='CARS',STATUS='OLD')
    5 READ (10,*,END=50) FILEID, BEGIN, END, FLOW
        IF (FILEID.EQ.ID) THEN
            TOTMIN = TOTMIN + MINUTE(BEGIN,END)
            TOTCAR = TOTCAR + FLOW
        ENDIF
        I = 1
        COUNTD = .FALSE.
   10   IF (INTER(I).NE.99.AND..NOT.COUNTD) THEN
            IF (FILEID.NE.INTER(I)) THEN
                I = I + 1
            ELSE
                COUNTD = .TRUE.
            ENDIF
            GO TO 10
        ENDIF
        IF (.NOT.COUNTD) THEN
            INTER(I) = FILEID
            INTER(I+1) = 99
        ENDIF
        GO TO 5
   50 IF (TOTMIN.EQ.0) THEN
        PRINT 55, ID
   55   FORMAT (1X,'NO OBSERVATIONS FOR INTERSECTION ',I3)
      ELSE
        PRINT 60, ID
   60   FORMAT (1X,'INTERSECTION ',I3)
        PRINT 65, REAL(TOTCAR)/REAL(TOTMIN)
   65   FORMAT (1X,'AVERAGE CARS PER MINUTE = ',F5.2)
      ENDIF
      I = 0
   70 IF (INTER(I).NE.99) THEN
        I = I + 1
        GO TO 70
      ENDIF
      PRINT 75, I-1
```

171

```
        75 FORMAT (1X,I3,' INTERSECTIONS ARE REPRESENTED BY ',
       +           'THE DATA FILE')
*
        END
*------------------------------------------------------------*
        (no changes in function MINUTE)
*------------------------------------------------------------*
```

15.   Solution in text.

16.
```
*------------------------------------------------------------*
        INTEGER  FUNCTION  MAXI(K)
*
*   This subprogram returns the maximum value in an array.
*
        INTEGER  K(100), I
*
        MAXI = K(1)
        DO 5 I = 2,100
           IF (K(I).GT.MAXI) MAXI = K(I)
      5 CONTINUE
*
        RETURN
        END
*------------------------------------------------------------*
```

17.
```
*------------------------------------------------------------*
        INTEGER FUNCTION  MINI(K)
*
*   This function determines the minimum
*   value in an integer array of 100 elements.
*
        INTEGER  K(100), I
*
        MINI = K(1)
        DO 10 I=2,100
           IF (K(I).LT.MINI) MINI = K(I)
     10 CONTINUE
*
        RETURN
        END
*------------------------------------------------------------*
```

18.
```
*------------------------------------------------------------*
        INTEGER  FUNCTION  NPOS(K)
*
*   This subprogram returns the number of values equal
*   or greater than zero.
*
        INTEGER  K(100), I
*
        NPOS = 0
        DO 5 I = 1,100
           IF (K(I).GE.0) NPOS = NPOS + 1
      5 CONTINUE
```

```
      *
       RETURN
       END
*-----------------------------------------------------------*


19.  *-----------------------------------------------------------*
       INTEGER FUNCTION  NNEG(K)
      *
      * This function counts the number of negative
      * values in an integer array of 100 elements.
      *
       INTEGER  K(100), I
      *
       NNEG = 0
       DO 10 I=1,100
          IF (K(I).LT.0) NNEG = NNEG + 1
    10 CONTINUE
      *
       RETURN
       END
*-----------------------------------------------------------*


20.  *-----------------------------------------------------------*
       INTEGER  FUNCTION  NZERO(K)
      *
      * This subprogram returns the number of values equal to zero.
      *
       INTEGER  K(100), I
      *
       NZERO = 0
       DO 5 I = 1,100
          IF (K(I).EQ.0) NZERO = NZERO + 1
     5 CONTINUE
      *
       RETURN
       END
*-----------------------------------------------------------*


21.    ALPHA = (6.9 + Y)/DENOM(Y)
       PRINT 10, ALPHA
    10 FORMAT (1X,'ANSWER = ',F8.2)

22.    BETA = SIN(Y)/DEMON(Y**2)
       PRINT 5, BETA
     5 FORMAT (1X,'ANSWER = ',F8.2)

23.    GAMMA = SIN(Y)/DENOM(Y*Y)
       PRINT 10, GAMMA
    10 FORMAT (1X,'ANSWER = ',F8.2)

24.    DELTA = 1.0/DEMON(SIN(Y))
       PRINT 5, DELTA
     5 FORMAT (1X,'ANSWER = ',F8.2)

25. Solution in text.
```

26.
```
*-------------------------------------------------------------*
          INTEGER FUNCTION FACT(N)
     *
     * This function returns the value of n factorial.
     *
          INTEGER  I, N
     *
          IF (N.LT.0) THEN
             FACT = 0
          ELSE
             FACT = 1
             DO 10 I = 1, N
                FACT = FACT*I
     10     CONTINUE
          ENDIF
     *
          RETURN
          END
*-------------------------------------------------------------*
```

27.
```
*-------------------------------------------------------------*
          INTEGER FUNTION  ITOTAL(HR,MIN,SEC)
     *
     *  This function computes the total number
     *  of seconds in HR, MIN, SEC.
     *
          INTEGER  HR, MIN, SEC
     *
          ITOTAL = HR*60*60 + MIN*60 + SEC
     *
          RETURN
          END
*-------------------------------------------------------------*
```

28.
```
*-------------------------------------------------------------*
          REAL FUNCTION COSX(X)
     *
     *  This function computes the cosine of x using a series
     *  representation.
     *
          INTEGER  K, FACT
     *
          COSX = 1
     *
          DO 20 K = 1, 9
             COSX = COSX + (-1)**K*X**(2*K)/FACT(2*K)
     20 CONTINUE
     *
          RETURN
          END
*-------------------------------------------------------------*
```

29.
```
*-------------------------------------------------------------*
          REAL FUNCTION COSX(X)
     *
```

```
*   This function computes the cosine of x using a series
*   representation, using as many terms of the series as
*   are necessary to ensure that the absolute value of the
*   last term used is less than 0.000001.
*
      INTEGER  N
      REAL  X, TERM
*
      N = 1
      COSX = 1
      TERM = 1
    5 IF (ABS(TERM.GE.0.1E-05)) THEN
         N = N + 1
         TERM = (-1)**(N-1)*X**(2*(N-1))/FACT(2*(N-1))
         COSX = COSX + TERM
         GO TO 5
      ENDIF
*
      RETURN
      END
*-------------------------------------------------------------*
```

30.
```
*-------------------------------------------------------------*
      PROGRAM COMPAR
*
*   This program compares the cosine computed with a
*   series representation to that computed from the intrinsic
*   function.
*
      INTEGER  I
      REAL  RADIAN, COSX
*
      PRINT 5
    5 FORMAT ('1', 13X, 'COSINE COMPARISON'//
     +          1X, 'RADIANS', 5X, 'INTRINSINC FUNCTION', 5X,
     +          1X, 'SERIES SUMMATION'/)
*
      RADIAN = 0.0
*
      DO 20 I = 1, 32
         PRINT 15, RADIAN, COS(RADIAN), COSX(RADIAN)
   15    FORMAT(1X, F5.1, 11X, F9.7, 14X, F9.7)
         RADIAN = RADIAN + 0.1
   20 CONTINUE
*
      END
*-------------------------------------------------------------*
```

1.

```
*-------------------------------------------------------------*
      PROGRAM  SIGGEN
*
*  This program generates a signal composed
*  of a sine wave plus random noise.
*
      INTEGER  SEED, I
      REAL  PI, T, NOISE, X
      DATA  PI, T /3.141593, 0.0/
*
      PRINT*, 'ENTER A POSITIVE INTEGER SEED: '
      READ*, SEED
      OPEN (UNIT=15,FILE='SIGNAL',STATUS='NEW')
*
      DO 10 I=1,101
         CALL RANDOM (SEED, NOISE)
         X = 2*SIN(2*PI*T) + NOISE
         WRITE (15,*) T, X
         T = T + 0.25
   10 CONTINUE
*
      END
*-------------------------------------------------------------*
      (no change in subroutine RANDOM)
*-------------------------------------------------------------*
```

2.

```
*-------------------------------------------------------------*
      PROGRAM  SIGGEN
*
*  This program generates a signal composed
*  of a sine wave plus random noise.
*
      INTEGER  SEED, I
      REAL  PI, T, NOISE, X, INCR
      DATA  PI, T /3.141593, 0.0/
*
      PRINT*, 'ENTER A POSITIVE INTEGER SEED: '
      READ*, SEED
      PRINT*, 'ENTER THE TIME INCREMENT: '
      READ*, INCR
      OPEN (UNIT=15,FILE='SIGNAL',STATUS='NEW')
*
      DO 10 I=1,101
         CALL RANDOM (SEED, NOISE)
         X = 2*SIN(2*PI*T) + NOISE
         WRITE (15,*) T, X
         T = T + INCR
   10 CONTINUE
*
      END
*-------------------------------------------------------------*
      (no changes in subroutine RANDOM)
*-------------------------------------------------------------*
```

3. Solution in text.

4.
```
*------------------------------------------------------------*
      PROGRAM  SIGGEN
*
*  This program generates a signal composed
*  of a sine wave plus random noise.
*
      INTEGER  SEED, I
      REAL  PI, T, NOISE, X, NCONST
      DATA  PI, T /3.141593, 0.0/
*
      PRINT*, 'ENTER A POSITIVE INTEGER SEED: '
      READ*, SEED
      PRINT*, 'ENTER NOISE CONSTANT: '
      READ*, NCONST
      OPEN (UNIT=15,FILE='SIGNAL',STATUS='NEW')
*
      DO 10 I=1,101
         CALL RANDOM (SEED, NOISE)
         X = 2*SIN(2*PI*T) + NOISE*NCONST
         WRITE (15,*) T, X
         T = T + 0.01
   10 CONTINUE
*
      END
*------------------------------------------------------------*
      (no changes in subroutine RANDOM)
*------------------------------------------------------------*
```

5.
```
*------------------------------------------------------------*
      PROGRAM  SIGGEN
*
*  This program generates a signal composed
*  of a sine wave plus random noise.
*
      INTEGER  SEED, I
      REAL  PI, T, NOISE, X
      DATA  PI, T /3.141593, 0.0/
*
      PRINT*, 'ENTER A POSITIVE INTEGER SEED: '
      READ*, SEED
      OPEN (UNIT=15,FILE='SIGNAL',STATUS='NEW')
*
      DO 10 I=1,101
         CALL RANDOM (SEED, NOISE)
         X = 2*COS(2*PI*T) + NOISE
         WRITE (15,*) T, X
         T = T + 0.01
   10 CONTINUE
*
      END
*------------------------------------------------------------*
      (no changes in subroutine RANDOM)
```

177

```
        *--------------------------------------------------------*
6.      *--------------------------------------------------------*
        PROGRAM  TEST
      *
      *  This program will test the delete subroutine.
      *
        INTEGER  LIST(501), I, OLD
      *
        PRINT*, 'ENTER LIST OF FIVE VALUES AND TRAILER: '
        READ*, (LIST(I),I=1,6)
        PRINT*, 'ENTER VALUE TO DELETE: '
        READ*, OLD
      5 IF  (OLD.GT.0)  THEN
          CALL DELETE (LIST, OLD)
          I = 1
     10     IF  (LIST(I).NE.999999999)  THEN
              PRINT*, LIST(I)
              I = I + 1
              GO TO 10
          ENDIF
          PRINT*, 'ENTER VALUE TO DELETE, ZERO TO QUIT: '
          READ*, OLD
          GO TO 5
        ENDIF
      *
        END
        *--------------------------------------------------------*
        (no changes in subroutine DELETE)
        *--------------------------------------------------------*

7.      *--------------------------------------------------------*
        SUBROUTINE  INSERT(SSN,NEW)
      *
      *  This subroutine will insert a new user in the SSN list.
      *
        INTEGER  SSN(501), NEW, I, CURRNT, TRAILR
      *
        I = 1
      5 IF (SSN(I).GT.NEW) THEN
          I = I + 1
          GO TO 5
        ENDIF
      *
        IF (SSN(I).EQ.NEW) THEN
          PRINT 10, NEW
     10     FORMAT (1X,I9,' IS ALREADY IN USER LIST')
        ELSE
          CURRNT = I
     15     IF (SSN(I).NE.0) THEN
              I = I + 1
              GO TO 15
          ENDIF
          TRAILR = I
          DO 20 I=TRAILR,CURRNT,-1
```

```
                    SSN(I+1) = SSN(I)
          20    CONTINUE
                SSN(CURRNT) = NEW
             ENDIF
      *
             RETURN
             END
      *----------------------------------------------------------*
```

8.
```
      *----------------------------------------------------------*
      *
             SUBROUTINE  DELETE(SSN,OLD)
      *
      * This subroutine will delete a old user in the SSN list.
      *
             INTEGER  SSN(501), OLD, I
      *
             I = 1
          5 IF (SSN(I).GT.OLD) THEN
                I = I + 1
                GO TO 5
             ENDIF
      *
             IF (SSN(I).LT.OLD) THEN
                PRINT 10, OLD
          10    FORMAT (1X,'USER ',I9,' NOT IN LIST')
             ELSE
          15    IF (SSN(I).NE.0) THEN
                   SSN(I) = SSN(I+1)
                   I = I + 1
                   GO TO 15
                ENDIF
             ENDIF
      *
             RETURN
             END
      *----------------------------------------------------------*
```

9.   Solution in text.

10.
```
      *----------------------------------------------------------*
      *
             SUBROUTINE  DELETE(SSN,OLD)
      *
      * This subroutine will delete a old user in the SSN list.
      *
             INTEGER  SSN(501), OLD, I, TOTAL
      *
             I = 1
          5 IF (SSN(I).LT.OLD) THEN
                I = I + 1
                GO TO 5
             ENDIF
      *
             IF (SSN(I).GT.OLD) THEN
```

179

```
                  PRINT 10, OLD
        10     FORMAT (1X,'USER ',I9,' NOT IN LIST')
            ELSE
        15     IF (SSN(I).NE.999999999) THEN
                  SSN(I) = SSN(I+1)
                  I = I + 1
                  GO TO 15
               ENDIF
            ENDIF
            TOTAL = I - 2
            PRINT 20, TOTAL
        20 FORMAT (1X,I5, ' RECORDS IN LIST,',
           +           ' NOT COUNTING THE TRAILER VALUE')
     *
            RETURN
            END
     *------------------------------------------------------------*
```

11.
```
     *------------------------------------------------------------*
            SUBROUTINE  SUBMAX(TIME)
     *
     * This subroutine subtracts the maximum
     * value in the array TIME from each element in the array.
     *
            INTEGER  I
            REAL  TIME(100), MAX
     *
            MAX = TIME(1)
            DO 10 I=2,100
               IF (TIME(I).GT.MAX) MAX = TIME(I)
        10 CONTINUE
            DO 20 I=1,100
               TIME(I) = TIME(I) - MAX
        20 CONTINUE
     *
            RETURN
            END
     *------------------------------------------------------------*
```

12.
```
     *------------------------------------------------------------*
            SUBROUTINE  ADD(TIME)
     *
     * This subroutine determines the minimum value in an
     * array, time, of 100 elements and adds that value to
     * each value in the array.
     *
            INTEGER  I
            REAL  TIME(100), MIN
     *
            MIN = TIME(1)
     *
            DO 10 I = 2, 100
               IF (TIME(I).LT.MIN)  MIN = TIME(I)
        10 CONTINUE
```

```
*
      DO 20 I = 1, 100
          TIME(I) = TIME(I) +  MIN
   20 CONTINUE
*
      RETURN
      END
*----------------------------------------------------------------*
```

13.
```
*----------------------------------------------------------------*
      SUBROUTINE   MODIFY(TIME)
*
*  This subroutine  replaces each negative
*  value in the array TIME with zero.
*
      INTEGER  I
      REAL  TIME(100)
*
      DO 10 I=1,100
          IF (TIME(I).LT.0.0) TIME(I) = 0.0
   10 CONTINUE
*
      RETURN
      END
*----------------------------------------------------------------*
```

14.
```
*----------------------------------------------------------------*
      SUBROUTINE   AVEVAL(TIME)
*
*  This subroutine determines the average value in the real
*  array, time.  A 1.0 is added to all the values above the
*  average and subtracted from all the values below the average.
*
      INTEGER  I
      REAL  TIME(100), SUM, AVE
*
      SUM = 0.0
*
      DO 10 I = 1, 100
          SUM = SUM + TIME(I)
   10 CONTINUE
*
      AVE = SUM/100.0
*
      DO 20 I = 1, 100
          IF (TIME(I).GT.AVE) THEN
              TIME(I) = TIME(I) + 1.0
          ELSEIF (TIME(I).LT.AVE) THEN
              TIME(I) = TIME(I) - 1.0
          ENDIF
   20 CONTINUE
*
      RETURN
      END
*----------------------------------------------------------------*
```

```
15.  *------------------------------------------------------------*
           SUBROUTINE  MODIFY(TIME)
     *
     *  This subroutine replaces each
     *  value in the array TIME with its absolute value.
     *
           INTEGER  I
           REAL  TIME(100)
     *
           DO 10 I=1,100
               TIME(I) = ABS(TIME(I))
        10 CONTINUE
     *
           RETURN
           END
     *------------------------------------------------------------*


16.  *------------------------------------------------------------*
           SUBROUTINE  ZERO(TIME, LZERO)
     *
     *  This subroutine returns a logical value of true if
     *  all the values in the array, time, are zero, and
     *  false otherwise.
     *
           INTEGER  I
           REAL  TIME(100)
           LOGICAL  LZERO
     *
           LZERO = .TRUE.
     *
           DO 10 I = 1, 100
               IF (TIME(I).NE.0.0) LZERO = .FALSE.
        10 CONTINUE
     *
           RETURN
           END
     *------------------------------------------------------------*


17.  *------------------------------------------------------------*
           SUBROUTINE  ABSOL(Z,W)
     *
     *  This subroutine puts the absolute value of
     *  each element of Z into the corresponding
     *  position of W.
     *
           INTEGER  I, J
           REAL  Z(5,4), W(5,4)
     *
           DO 10 I=1,5
               DO 5 J=1,4
                   W(I,J) = ABS(Z(I,J))
         5     CONTINUE
        10 CONTINUE
     *
```

```
      RETURN
      END
*------------------------------------------------------------*


18.  *------------------------------------------------------------*
      SUBROUTINE  SIGNS(Z, W)
*
*  This subroutine puts the sign (1.0, 0.0, -1.0)
*  of the elements of z into the corresponding positions
*  of w.
*
      INTEGER  I, J
      REAL  Z(5,4), W(5,4)
*
      DO 10 I = 1, 5
         DO 5 J = 1, 4
            IF (Z(I,J).GT.0.0) THEN
               W(I,J) = 1.0
            ELSEIF (Z(I,J).EQ.0.0) THEN
               W(I,J) = 0.0
            ELSE
               W(I,J) = -1.0
            ENDIF
    5     CONTINUE
   10 CONTINUE
*
      RETURN
      END
*------------------------------------------------------------*


19.  Solution in text.


20.  *------------------------------------------------------------*
      SUBROUTINE ROUND(Z, W)
*
*  This subroutine rounds each element of
*  z up to the next multiple of 10 and
*  stores that in the corresponding
*  position of w.
*
      INTEGER  I, J
      REAL  Z(5,4), W(5,4)
*
      DO 10 I = 1, 5
         DO 5 J = 1, 4
            IF ((INT(Z(I,J)/10))*10.0.EQ.Z(I,J)) THEN
               W(I,J) = Z(I,J)
            ELSE
               IF (Z(I,J).LT.0.0) THEN
                  W(I,J) = INT(Z(I,J))/10*10.0
               ELSE
                  W(I,J) = INT(Z(I,J) + 10.0)/10*10.0
               ENDIF
            ENDIF
    5     CONTINUE
```

```
      10 CONTINUE
      *
         RETURN
         END
      *--------------------------------------------------------*

21.   *--------------------------------------------------------*
         SUBROUTINE  RANGE(K,MAX,MIN)
      *
      *  This subroutine determines the maximum
      *  and minimum values in an integer array.
      *
         INTEGER  K(50), I, MAX, MIN
      *
         MAX = K(1)
         MIN = K(1)
         DO 10 I=2,50
            IF (K(I).GT.MAX) MAX = K(I)
            IF (K(I).LT.MIN) MIN = K(I)
      10 CONTINUE
      *
         RETURN
         END
      *--------------------------------------------------------*

22.   *--------------------------------------------------------*
         SUBROUTINE  TEST(NUM, AVE)
      *
      *  This subroutine reads test scores until
      *  it encounters a negative score.  It returns
      *  the number of test scores read before the negative
      *  value was encountered and the average test score.
      *
         INTEGER  NUM, SCORE
         REAL  AVE, SUM
      *
         NUM = 0
         SUM = 0.0
      *
         READ(12,*) SCORE
      *
       5 IF (SCORE.LT.0.0) THEN
            NUM = NUM + 1
            SUM = SUM + SCORE
            READ(12,*) SCORE
            GO TO 5
         ENDIF
      *
         AVE = SUM/REAL(NUM)
      *
         RETURN
         END
      *--------------------------------------------------------*

23.   *--------------------------------------------------------*
```

```
      SUBROUTINE  STAT1(X,AVE,VAR,SD)
*
* This subroutine computes the average,
* variance, and standard deviation of
* an array of 100 values.
*
      INTEGER  I
      REAL  X(100), AVE, VAR, SD, SUM
*
      SUM = 0.0
      DO 10 I=1,100
         SUM = SUM + X(I)
   10 CONTINUE
      AVE = SUM/100.0
      SUM = 0.0
      DO 20 I=1,100
         SUM = SUM + (AVE-X(I))**2
   20 CONTINUE
      VAR = SUM/99.0
      SD = SQRT(VAR)
*
      RETURN
      END
*-----------------------------------------------------------*
```

24.
```
*-----------------------------------------------------------*
      SUBROUTINE  STAT2(X, N, AVE, VAR, SD)
*
* This subroutine computes the average,
* variance, and standard deviation of an
* array of n values.
*
      INTEGER  I, N
      REAL  X(N), AVE, VAR, SD, SUM
*
      SUM = 0.0
      DO 10 I = 1, N
         SUM = SUM + X(I)
   10 CONTINUE
*
      AVE = SUM/REAL(N)
*
      SUM = 0.0
      DO 20 I = 1, N
         SUM = SUM + (AVE - X(I))**2
   20 CONTINUE
*
      VAR = SUM/REAL(N-1)
*
      SD = SQRT(VAR)
*
      RETURN
      END
*-----------------------------------------------------------*
```

25.   *---*
          SUBROUTINE BIAS(X, Y, N)
      *
      * This subroutine sutracts the minimum value of x
      * from each element and stroe the result in y.
      *
          INTEGER I, N
          REAL X(N), Y(N), XMIN
      *
          XMIN = X(1)
          DO 10 I = 2, N
              IF (X(I).LT.XMIN) XMIN = X(I)
       10 CONTINUE
      *
          DO 20 I = 1, N
              Y(I) = X(I) - XMIN
       20 CONTINUE
      *
          RETURN
          END

1.
```
*-------------------------------------------------------------*
      SUBROUTINE  GRAPH(VALUE,N,LINE)
*
* This subroutine prints a bar graph using an array
* of N elements with a maximum line size.
*
      INTEGER  N, LINE, I, K
      REAL  VALUE(N), MAX, SCALE
      LOGICAL  NEGNUM
      CHARACTER*130  BAR
*
* FIND MAXIMUM AND CHECK FOR ERROR CONDITIONS
*
      IF (LINE.GT.130.OR.LINE.LT.1) THEN
         PRINT*, 'LINE LENGTH ERROR ',LINE
      ELSE
         NEGNUM = .FALSE.
         MAX = VALUE(1)
         DO 10 I=1,N
            IF (VALUE(I).LT.0.0) THEN
               NEGNUM = .TRUE.
            ELSE
               IF (VALUE(I).GT.MAX) MAX = VALUE(I)
            ENDIF
10       CONTINUE
*
* FILL BAR WITH ASTERISKS
*
         IF (.NOT.NEGNUM) THEN
            DO 20 I=1,LINE
               BAR(I:I) = '*'
20          CONTINUE
*
* SCALE DATA VALUES AND PRINT BAR
*
            SCALE = REAL(LINE)/MAX
            DO 30 I=1,N
               K = NINT(VALUE(I)*SCALE)
               PRINT*, BAR(1:K)
               PRINT*, BAR(1:K)
30          CONTINUE
         ENDIF
      ENDIF
*
      RETURN
      END
*-------------------------------------------------------------*
```

2.
```
*-------------------------------------------------------------*
      SUBROUTINE  GRAPH(VALUE,N,LINE)
*
* This subroutine prints a bar graph using an array
* of N elements with a maximum line size.
```

```
*
          INTEGER  N, LINE, I, K
          REAL  VALUE(N), MAX, SCALE
          LOGICAL  NEGNUM
          CHARACTER*130  BAR
*
*    Find maximum and check for error conditions.
*
          IF (LINE.GT.130.OR.LINE.LT.1) THEN
             PRINT*, 'LINE LENGTH ERROR ',LINE
          ELSE
             NEGNUM = .FALSE.
             MAX = VALUE(1)
             DO 10 I=1,N
                IF (VALUE(I).LT.0.0) THEN
                   NEGNUM = .TRUE.
                ELSE
                   IF (VALUE(I).GT.MAX) MAX = VALUE(I)
                ENDIF
   10        CONTINUE
*
*    Fill bar with asterisks.
*
             IF (.NOT.NEGNUM) THEN
                DO 20 I=1,LINE
                   BAR(I:I) = '*'
   20           CONTINUE
*
*    Scale data values and print bar.
*
                SCALE = REAL(LINE)/MAX
                DO 30 I=1,N
                   K = NINT(VALUE(I)*SCALE)
                   PRINT*, BAR(1:K)
                   PRINT*, BAR(1:K)
                   PRINT*, BAR(1:K)
                   PRINT*
   30           CONTINUE
             ENDIF
          ENDIF
*
          RETURN
          END
*------------------------------------------------------------*
```

3. Solution in text.

4.  ```
--
          PROGRAM DECODE
*
*   This program aids in deocding a message by counting
*   the number of occurrences of specified characters
*   in the message.
*
          INTEGER N, I, J, NUM, K
```
```

```
      REAL   SUM(30)
      CHARACTER*50  TEXT
      CHARACTER*1 CHAR(30)
      DATA  SUM /30*0.0/
*
*  Get the characters to be counted.
*
      PRINT*, 'ENTER THE NUMBER OF CHARACTERS TO BE COUNTED'
      READ*, NUM
      DO 2 I = 1,NUM
         PRINT 1, I
    1    FORMAT (1X, 'ENTER CHARACTER NUMBER ',I2,' : ')
         READ*, CHAR(I)
    2 CONTINUE
*
      OPEN (UNIT=10,FILE='SECRET',STATUS='OLD')
      READ (10,*) N
      DO 10 I=1,N
         READ (10,*) TEXT
         DO 5 J=1,50
            DO 3 K = 1,NUM
               IF (TEXT(J:J).EQ.CHAR(K)) SUM(K) = SUM(K) + 1
    3       CONTINUE
    5    CONTINUE
   10 CONTINUE
*
      PRINT*, 'TOTAL NUMBER OF CHARACTERS = ',N*50
      PRINT*
      PRINT*, 'OCCURRENCES OF CHARACTERS:'
      DO 12 I = 1,NUM
         PRINT 15, CHAR(I), SUM(I)
   15    FORMAT (1X,A,': = ',F6.0)
   12 CONTINUE
      PRINT*
      CALL GRAPH (SUM,NUM,20)
*
      END
*--------------------------------------------------------------*
      (no changes in subroutine GRAPH)
*--------------------------------------------------------------*
```

5.
```
  *--------------------------------------------------------------*
  *
      SUBROUTINE  GRAPH(VALUE,N,LINE)
  *
  * This subroutine prints a bar graph using an array
  * of N elements with a maximum line size.
  *
      INTEGER  N, LINE, I, J, K
      REAL   VALUE(N), MAX, SCALE, AVE
      LOGICAL  NEGNUM
      CHARACTER*130  BAR
  *
  * Find maximum and check for error conditions.
  *
```

189

```
            IF (LINE.GT.130.OR.LINE.LT.1) THEN
                PRINT*, 'LINE LENGTH ERROR ', LINE
            ELSE
                NEGNUM = .FALSE.
                MAX = VALUE(1)
                AVE = 0.0
                DO 10 I=1,N
                    IF (VALUE(I).LT.0.0) THEN
                        NEGNUM = .TRUE.
                    ELSE
                        IF (VALUE(I).GT.MAX) MAX = VALUE(I)
                    ENDIF
                    AVE = AVE + VALUE(I)
    10          CONTINUE
                AVE = AVE/REAL(N)
*
*  Scale data and print bar.
*
                IF (.NOT.NEGNUM) THEN
                    SCALE = REAL(LINE)/MAX
                    AVE = AVE*SCALE
                    DO 30 I=1,N
                        K = NINT(VALUE(I)*SCALE)
                        IF (K.LE.NINT(AVE)) THEN
                            DO 20 J=1,K
                                BAR(J:J) = '*'
    20                      CONTINUE
                        ELSE
                            DO 25 J=1,NINT(AVE)
                                BAR(J:J) = '*'
    25                      CONTINUE
                            DO 28 J=NINT(AVE)+1,K
                                BAR(J:J) = '+'
    28                      CONTINUE
                        ENDIF
                        PRINT*, BAR(1:K)
    30              CONTINUE
                ENDIF
            ENDIF
*
        RETURN
        END
*------------------------------------------------------------*


6.  *------------------------------------------------------------*
        PROGRAM  TEMP
*
*  This program initializes the temperatures in a metal
*  plate and determines the equilibrium temperatures
*  based on a tolerance value.
*
        INTEGER  NROW, NCOL, I, J, ITERAT
        LOGICAL  EQUILB
        DOUBLE PRECISION  OLD(10,10), NEW(10,10), TOLNC,
```

190

```
     +                           TOP, BOT, LEFT, RIGHT
*
       PRINT*, 'ENTER TEMPERATURE GRID SIZE:'
       PRINT*, 'ROWS, COLUMNS  (MAXIMUM 10,10) '
       READ*, NROW, NCOL
       PRINT*, 'ENTER ISOTHERMAL EDGE TEMPERATURES:'
       PRINT*, 'TOP, BOTTOM, LEFT, RIGHT '
       READ*, TOP, BOT, LEFT, RIGHT
       PRINT*, 'ENTER EQUILIBRIUM TOLERANCE VALUE: '
       READ*, TOLNC
*
*   Initialize temperature array.
*
       DO 5 J=1,NCOL
          NEW(1,J) = TOP
          NEW(NROW,J) = BOT
     5 CONTINUE
       DO 15 I=2,NROW-1
          NEW(I,1) = LEFT
          DO 10 J=2,NCOL-1
             NEW(I,J) = 0.0D+00
    10    CONTINUE
          NEW(I,NCOL) = RIGHT
    15 CONTINUE
       CALL MOVE(OLD,NEW,NROW,NCOL)
*
*   Print initial temperature array.
*
       PRINT*
       PRINT*, 'INITIAL TEMPERATURES'
       PRINT*
       CALL PRINT(OLD,NROW,NCOL)
*
*   Update temperatures until equilibrium.
*
       ITERAT = 0
       EQUILB = .FALSE.
    20 IF (.NOT.EQUILB) THEN
          ITERAT = ITERAT + 1
          EQUILB = .TRUE.
          DO 30 I=2,NROW-1
             DO 25 J=2,NCOL-1
                NEW(I,J) = (OLD(I-1,J) + OLD(I+1,J) +
     +                      OLD(I,J 1) + OLD(I,J+1))/4.0+00
                IF (DABS(NEW(I,J) - OLD(I,J)).GT.TOLNC)
     +                      EQUILB = .FALSE.
    25       CONTINUE
    30    CONTINUE
          CALL MOVE(OLD,NEW,NROW,NCOL)
          GO TO 20
       ENDIF
*
*   Print equilibrium temperature array.
*
       PRINT*
```

```
          PRINT*, 'EQUILBRIUM TEMPERATURES'
          PRINT*
          CALL PRINT(OLD,NROW,NCOL)
   *
          PRINT*
          PRINT 35, ITERAT
       35 FORMAT (1X,'THE NUMBER OF ITERATIONS TO REACH ',
        +          'EQUILIBRIUM = ',I3)
   *
          END
   *-------------------------------------------------------------*
          (no changes in subroutine PRINT)
   *-------------------------------------------------------------*
          (no changes in subroutine MOVE)
   *-------------------------------------------------------------*
```

7. Solution in text.

8.
```
   *-------------------------------------------------------------*
          PROGRAM  TEMP
   *
   * This program initializes the temperatures in a metal
   * plate and determines the equilibrium temperatures
   * based on a tolerance value.
   *
          INTEGER  NROW, NCOL, I, J
          LOGICAL  EQUILB
          DOUBLE PRECISION  OLD(10,10), NEW(10,10), TOLNC,
        +                   TOP, BOT, LEFT, RIGHT
   *
          PRINT*, 'ENTER TEMPERATURE GRID SIZE:'
          PRINT*, 'ROWS, COLUMNS  (MAXIMUM 10,10) '
          READ*, NROW, NCOL
          PRINT*, 'ENTER ISOTHERMAL EDGE TEMPERATURES:'
          PRINT*, 'TOP, BOTTOM, LEFT, RIGHT '
          READ*, TOP, BOT, LEFT, RIGHT
          PRINT*, 'ENTER EQUILIBRIUM TOLERANCE VALUE: '
          READ*, TOLNC
   *
   * Initialize temperature array.
   *
          DO 5 J=1,NCOL
             NEW(1,J) = TOP
             NEW(NROW,J) = BOT
        5 CONTINUE
          DO 15 I=2,NROW-1
             NEW(I,1) = LEFT
             DO 10 J=2,NCOL-1
                NEW(I,J) = 0.0D+00
       10    CONTINUE
             NEW(I,NCOL) = RIGHT
       15 CONTINUE
          CALL MOVE(OLD,NEW,NROW,NCOL)
   *
   * Print initial temperature array.
```

192

```
*
      PRINT*
      PRINT*, 'INITIAL TEMPERATURES'
      PRINT*
      CALL PRINT(OLD,NROW,NCOL)
*
*  Update temperatures until equilibrium.
*
      EQUILB = .FALSE.
   20 IF (.NOT.EQUILB) THEN
         EQUILB = .TRUE.
         CALL NEWTMP(NROW,NCOL,OLD,NEW,EQUILB,TOLNC)
         CALL MOVE(OLD,NEW,NROW,NCOL)
         GO TO 20
      ENDIF
*
*  Print equilibrium temperature array.
*
      PRINT*
      PRINT*, 'EQUILBRIUM TEMPERATURES'
      PRINT*
      CALL PRINT(OLD,NROW,NCOL)
*
      END
*--------------------------------------------------------------*
      SUBROUTINE NEWTMP(NROW,NCOL,OLD,NEW,EQUILB,TOLNC)
*
*  This subroutine calculates the new temperatures
*  in the grid.
*
      INTEGER NROW, NCOL, I, J
      LOGICAL EQUILB
      DOUBLE PRECISION  OLD(10,10), NEW(10,10), TOLNC
*
      DO 30 I=2,NROW-1
         DO 25 J=2,NCOL-1
            NEW(I,J) = (OLD(I-1,J) + OLD(I+1,J) +
     +                  OLD(I,J-1) + OLD(I,J+1))/4.0+00
            IF (DABS(NEW(I,J) - OLD(I,J)).GT.TOLNC)
     +                  EQUILB = .FALSE.
   25    CONTINUE
   30 CONTINUE
*
      RETURN
      END
*--------------------------------------------------------------*
      (no changes in subroutine PRINT)
*--------------------------------------------------------------*
      (no changes in subroutine MOVE)
*--------------------------------------------------------------*
```

9.

```
*--------------------------------------------------------------*
      PROGRAM  TEMP
*
*  This program initializes the temperatures in a metal
```

```
*   plate and determines the equilibrium temperatures
*   based on a tolerance value.
*

        INTEGER  NROW, NCOL, I, J, COUNT
        LOGICAL  EQUILB
        DOUBLE PRECISION  OLD(10,10), NEW(10,10), TOLNC,
       +                  TOP, BOT, LEFT, RIGHT
*
        PRINT*, 'ENTER TEMPERATURE GRID SIZE:'
        PRINT*, 'ROWS, COLUMNS  (MAXIMUM 10,10) '
        READ*, NROW, NCOL
        PRINT*, 'ENTER ISOTHERMAL EDGE TEMPERATURES:'
        PRINT*, 'TOP, BOTTOM, LEFT, RIGHT '
        READ*, TOP, BOT, LEFT, RIGHT
        PRINT*, 'ENTER EQUILIBRIUM TOLERANCE VALUE: '
        READ*, TOLNC
*
*   Initialize temperature array.
*
        DO 5 J=1,NCOL
            NEW(1,J) = TOP
            NEW(NROW,J) = BOT
     5  CONTINUE
        DO 15 I=2,NROW-1
            NEW(I,1) = LEFT
            DO 10 J=2,NCOL-1
                NEW(I,J) = 0.0D+00
    10      CONTINUE
            NEW(I,NCOL) = RIGHT
    15  CONTINUE
        CALL MOVE(OLD,NEW,NROW,NCOL)
*
*   Print initial temperature array.
*
        PRINT*
        PRINT*, 'INITIAL TEMPERATURES'
        PRINT*
        CALL PRINT(OLD,NROW,NCOL)
*
*   Update temperatures until equilibrium.
*
        COUNT = 0
        EQUILB = .FALSE.
    20 IF (.NOT.EQUILB.AND.COUNT.LE.10) THEN
            EQUILB = .TRUE.
            DO 30 I=2,NROW-1
                DO 25 J=2,NCOL-1
                    NEW(I,J) = (OLD(I-1,J) + OLD(I+1,J) +
       +                        OLD(I,J-1) + OLD(I,J+1))/4.0+00
                    IF (DABS(NEW(I,J) - OLD(I,J)).GT.TOLNC)
       +                        EQUILB = .FALSE.
    25          CONTINUE
    30      CONTINUE
            CALL MOVE(OLD,NEW,NROW,NCOL)
            COUNT = COUNT + 1
```

```
            GO TO 20
         ENDIF
   *
   *  Print equilibrium temperature array.
   *
         PRINT*
         PRINT*, 'EQUILBRIUM TEMPERATURES'
         PRINT*
         CALL PRINT(OLD,NROW,NCOL)
   *
         END
   *----------------------------------------------------------*
         (no changes in subroutine PRINT)
   *----------------------------------------------------------*
         (no changes in subroutine MOVE)
   *----------------------------------------------------------*
```

10.

```
   *----------------------------------------------------------*
         PROGRAM  TEMP
   *
   *  This program initializes the temperatures in a metal
   *  plate and determines the equilibrium temperatures
   *  based on a tolerance value.
   *
         INTEGER  NROW, NCOL, I, J
         LOGICAL  EQUILB
         DOUBLE PRECISION  OLD(10,10), NEW(10,10), TOLNC,
        +                  TOP, BOT, LEFT, RIGHT
   *
         PRINT*, 'ENTER TEMPERATURE GRID SIZE:'
         PRINT*, 'ROWS, COLUMNS  (MAXIMUM 10,10)'
         READ*, NROW, NCOL
         PRINT*, 'ENTER ISOTHERMAL EDGE TEMPERATURES:'
         PRINT*, 'TOP, BOTTOM, LEFT, RIGHT'
         READ*, TOP, BOT, LEFT, RIGHT
         PRINT*, 'ENTER EQUILIBRIUM TOLERANCE VALUE'
         READ*, TOLNC
   *
   *  Initialize temperature array.
   *
         DO 5 J=1,NCOL
            NEW(1,J) = TOP
            NEW(NROW,J) = BOT
       5 CONTINUE
         DO 15 I=2,NROW-1
            NEW(I,1) = LEFT
            DO 10 J=2,NCOL-1
               NEW(I,J) = 0.0D+00
      10    CONTINUE
            NEW(I,NCOL) = RIGHT
      15 CONTINUE
         CALL MOVE (OLD,NEW,NROW,NCOL)
   *
   *  Print initial temperature array.
   *
```

195

```
      PRINT*
      PRINT*, 'INITIAL TEMPERATURES'
      PRINT*
      CALL PRINT (OLD,NROW,NCOL)
*
*  Update temperatures until equilibrium.
*
      EQUILB = .FALSE.
   20 IF (.NOT.EQUILB) THEN
         EQUILB = .TRUE.
         DO 30 I=2,NROW-1
            DO 25 J=2,NCOL-1
               NEW(I,J) = (OLD(I-1,J) + OLD(I+1,J) +
     +                      OLD(I,J-1) + OLD(I,J+1))/4.0D+00
               IF (DABS(NEW(I,J) - OLD(I,J)).GT.TOLNC)
     +                      EQUILB = .FALSE.
   25       CONTINUE
   30    CONTINUE
         CALL MOVE (OLD,NEW,NROW,NCOL)
         GO TO 20
      ENDIF
*
*  Print equilibrium temperature array.
*
      PRINT*
      PRINT*, 'EQUILBRIUM TEMPERATURES'
      PRINT*
      CALL PRINT (OLD,NROW,NCOL)
*
      END
*-------------------------------------------------------------------
      (no changes in subroutine MOVE)
*-------------------------------------------------------------------
*
      SUBROUTINE  PRINT(OLD,NROW,NCOL)
*
*  This subroutine prints a double precision
*  array with NROW rows and NCOL columns.
*
      INTEGER  NROW, NCOL, I, J
      DOUBLE PRECISION  OLD(10,10), MAX, MIN
*
      MAX = OLD(1,1)
      MIN = OLD(1,1)
      DO 2 I=1,NROW
         DO 1 J=1,NCOL
            IF (OLD(I,J).GT.MAX)  MAX = OLD(I,J)
            IF (OLD(I,J).LT.MIN)  MIN = OLD(I,J)
    1    CONTINUE
    2 CONTINUE
*
      DO 10 I=1,NROW
         PRINT 5, (OLD(I,J),J=1,NCOL)
    5    FORMAT(1X,10(D12.5,1X))
   10 CONTINUE
```

```
      *
          PRINT 15, MAX
       15 FORMAT (1X,/,'THE MAXIMUM WAS ',D12.5,' AND OCCURRED IN ',
          +         'POSITIONS: ')
          DO 30 I = 1,NROW
             DO 25 J = 1,NCOL
                IF (OLD(I,J).EQ.MAX) PRINT 20, I, J
       20         FORMAT(1X,10X,'(',I2,',',I2,')')
       25    CONTINUE
       30 CONTINUE
          PRINT 35, MIN
       35 FORMAT (1X,'THE MINIMUM WAS ',D12.5,' AND OCCURRED IN ',
          +         'POSITIONS: ')
          DO 50 I = 1,NROW
             DO 45 J = 1,NCOL
                IF (OLD(I,J).EQ.MIN) PRINT 40, I, J
       40         FORMAT(1X,10X,'(',I2,',',I2.')')
       45    CONTINUE
       50 CONTINUE
      *
          RETURN
          END
      *--------------------------------------------------------------*
```

11.
```
      *--------------------------------------------------------------*
          PROGRAM  ELECT1
      *
      * This program determines the magnitude and phase
      * of an RC circuit on a sine wave.
      *
          REAL  R, C, W, MAGN, PHASE, DEGREE
          COMPLEX  I, HW
      *
          I = (0.0, 1.0)
      *
          PRINT*, 'ENTER RESISTANCE IN OHMS'
          READ*, R
          PRINT*, 'ENTER CAPACITANCE IN FARADS'
          READ*, C
          PRINT*, 'ENTER THE SINE FREQUENCY IN RADIANS PER SEC'
          READ*, W
      *
          HW = (I*W*R*C)/(1.0 + I*W*R*C)
          MAGN = CABS(HW)
          PHASE = ATAN(AIMAG(HW)/REAL(HW))
          DEGREE = PHASE*(180.0/3.141593)
      *
          PRINT 5, MAGN, DEGREE
        5 FORMAT (1X,'MAGNITUDE EFFECT:',F5.2,3X,
          +          'PHASE EFFECT IN DEGREES:', F5.2)
      *
          END
      *--------------------------------------------------------------*
```

12.
```
      *--------------------------------------------------------------*
```

197

```
          PROGRAM  ELECT1
      *
      *  This program determines the magnitude and phase
      *  of an RC circuit on a sine wave.
      *
          REAL  R, C, W, MAGN, PHASE
          COMPLEX  I, HW
      *
          I = (0.0, 1.0)
      *
          PRINT*, 'ENTER RESISTANCE IN KILO-OHMS'
          READ*, R
          PRINT*, 'ENTER CAPACITANCE IN FARADS'
          READ*, C
          PRINT*, 'ENTER THE SINE FREQUENCY IN RADIANS PER SEC'
          READ*, W
      *
          HW = (I*W*R*1000.0*C)/(1.0 + I*W*R*1000.0*C)
          MAGN = CABS(HW)
          PHASE = ATAN(AIMAG(HW)/REAL(HW))
      *
          PRINT 5, MAGN, PHASE
        5 FORMAT (1X,'MAGNITUDE EFFECT:',F5.2,3X,
          +              'PHASE EFFECT:', F5.2)
      *
          END
      *-------------------------------------------------------------*

13.  Solution in text.

14.  *-------------------------------------------------------------*
          PROGRAM  ELECT1
      *
      *  This program determines the magnitude and phase
      *  of an RC circuit on a sine wave.
      *
          REAL  R, C, W, MAGN, PHASE, F
          COMPLEX  I, HW
      *
          I = (0.0, 1.0)
      *
          PRINT*, 'ENTER RESISTANCE IN OHMS'
          READ*, R
          PRINT*, 'ENTER CAPACITANCE IN FARADS'
          READ*, C
          PRINT*, 'ENTER THE SINE FREQUENCY IN HERTZ'
          READ*, F
      *
          W = 2*3.14159*F
          HW = (I*W*R*C)/(1.0 + I*W*R*C)
          MAGN = CABS(HW)
          PHASE = ATAN(AIMAG(HW)/REAL(HW))
      *
          PRINT 5, MAGN, PHASE
        5 FORMAT (1X,'MAGNITUDE EFFECT:',F5.2,3X,
```

```
     +                'PHASE EFFECT:', F5.2)
*
      END
*------------------------------------------------------------*


15. *------------------------------------------------------------*
      PROGRAM   ELECT1
*
*  This program determines the magnitude and phase
*  of an RC circuit on a sine wave.
*
      REAL  R, C, W, MAGN, PHASE
      COMPLEX  I, HW
*
      I = (0.0, 1.0)
*
      PRINT*, 'ENTER RESISTANCE IN OHMS'
      READ*, R
      PRINT*, 'ENTER CAPACITANCE IN FARADS'
      READ*, C
      PRINT*, 'ENTER THE SINE FREQUENCY IN RADIANS PER SEC'
      READ*, W
*
    1 IF (W.GE.0.0) THEN
         HW = (I*W*R*C)/(1.0 + I*W*R*C)
         MAGN = CABS(HW)
         PHASE = ATAN(AIMAG(HW)/REAL(HW))
*
         PRINT 5, MAGN, PHASE
    5    FORMAT (1X,'MAGNITUDE EFFECT:',F5.2,3X,
     +               'PHASE EFFECT:', F5.2)
         PRINT*, 'ENTER THE SINE FREQUENCY IN RADIANS PER SEC: '
         READ*, W
         GO TO 1
      ENDIF
*
      END
*------------------------------------------------------------*


16. *------------------------------------------------------------*
      PROGRAM   LABEL
*
*  This program reads name and address information
*  and prints labels.
*
      INTEGER  I, K
      CHARACTER*10  FIRST, CITY
      CHARACTER*6  MIDDLE
      CHARACTER*21  LAST
      CHARACTER*25  ADDRES
      CHARACTER*2  STATE
      CHARACTER*5  ZIP
*
      OPEN(UNIT=12, FILE='ADDR', STATUS='old')
*
```

```
          DO 30 I = 1, 50
*
          READ(12,5) FIRST, MIDDLE, LAST
     5    FORMAT(A10, 4X, A6, 4X, A21)
          READ(12,10) ADDRES, CITY, STATE, ZIP
    10    FORMAT(A25, 4X, A10, 5X, A2, 3X, A5)
*
          PRINT 15, FIRST(1:1), MIDDLE(1:1), LAST
    15    FORMAT(1X, A1, '. ', A1, '. ', A21)
          PRINT 20, ADDRES
    20    FORMAT(1X, A25)
          K = INDEX(CITY, ' ')-1
          IF (K.LT.1) K = 10
          PRINT 25, CITY(1:K)//', '//STATE//'  '//ZIP
    25    FORMAT(1X, A////)
    30 CONTINUE
*
       END
*------------------------------------------------------------*
```

17. Solution in text.

18.
```
*------------------------------------------------------------*
       PROGRAM DPSIN
*
*  This program uses a series expansion
*  to compute a double-precision sine value.
*
       INTEGER  K
       DOUBLE PRECISION  DX, DPSUM, TERM
*
       READ*, DX
*
       K = 1
       DPSUM = 0.0D+00
       TERM = DX
    20 IF (DABS(TERM).GE.1.0D-09) THEN
          DPSUM = DPSUM + (-1)**(K-1)*TERM
          TERM = TERM*DX**2/((2*K)*(2*K + 1))
          K = K + 1
          GO TO 20
       ENDIF
*
       PRINT 30, DPSUM, DSIN(DX)
    30 FORMAT(1X, 'SERIES EVALUATION = ', D21.4/
      +        1X, 'INTRINSIC FUNCTION = ', D21.4)
*
       END
*------------------------------------------------------------
```

19.
```
*------------------------------------------------------------*
       PROGRAM  QUAD
*
*  This program computes the roots
*  of a quadratic equation.
```

```
*
      REAL   A, B, C
      COMPLEX  X1, X2, DISCR
*
      READ*, A, B, C
*
      IF (A.EQ.0.0) THEN
         PRINT 10
10       FORMAT(1X, 'COEFFICIENT OF X*X IS ZERO')
         PRINT 11
11       FORMAT(1X, '(THE EQUATION IS LINEAR NOT QUADRATIC.)')
      ELSE
         DISCR = B*B - 4.0*A*C
         X1 = (-B + SQRT(DISCR))/(2.0D+00*A)
         X2 = (-B - SQRT(DISCR))/(2.0D+00*A)
         IF (REAL(DISCR).GE.0.0) THEN
            PRINT 20, REAL(X1), REAL(X2)
20          FORMAT(1X, 'X1 = ', F6.1/
     +             1X, 'X2 = ', F6.1)
         ELSE
            PRINT 25, X1, X2
25          FORMAT(1X, 'X1 = ', F6.1, '+I', F6.1/
     +             1X, 'X2 = ', F6.1, '+I', F6.1)
         ENDIF
      ENDIF
*
      END
*-------------------------------------------------------------*

20. *-------------------------------------------------------------*
      PROGRAM MAGNTD
*
* This program computes and prints the magnitude effects
* for 20 frequency points.
*
      REAL   MAG, OMEGA, PHASE
      COMPLEX  A, B, C, D, E, HOFW
*
      PRINT*, 'ENTER THE COEFFICIENTS, A, B, C, D, E...'
      READ*, A, B, C, D, E
      PRINT*, 'ENTER THE INPUT FREQUENCY'
      READ*, OMEGA
*
      HOFW = ((A*CMPLX(OMEGA)**2 + B*CMPLX(OMEGA) + C)
     +        /(CMPLX(OMEGA)**2 + D*CMPLX(OMEGA) + E))
      MAG = ABS(HOFW)
      PHASE = ATAN(AIMAG(HOFW)/REAL(HOFW))
      PRINT 15, OMEGA, MAG, PHASE
15 FORMAT(1X, 'OMEGA FOR THE TRANSFER FUNCTION', 9X, F5.1, /
     +        'MAGNITUDE OF THE TRANSFER FUNCTION ', 5X, F9.4, /
     +        'PHASE (IN RADIANS)                 ', 5X, F9.4)
*
      END
*-------------------------------------------------------------*
```

21.
```
*----------------------------------------------------------------*
      PROGRAM MAGNTD
*
*   This program computes and prints the magnitude effects
*   for 20 frequency points.
*
      REAL  MAG, OMEGA1, OMEGA2, OMEGA, INTRVL
      COMPLEX  A, B, C, D, E
*
      PRINT*, 'ENTER THE COEFFICIENTS, A, B, C, D, E...'
      READ*, A, B, C, D, E
      PRINT*, 'ENTER THE BEGINING AND ENDING FREQUENCIES'
      READ*, OMEGA1, OMEGA2
*
      PRINT*, 'MAGNITUDE EFFECTS FOR 20 FREQUENCY POINTS'
      PRINT*, 'OMEGA              MAGNITUDE'
      INTRVL = (ABS(OMEGA2 - OMEGA1)+1.0)/20.0
      OMEGA = OMEGA1
*
   10 IF (OMEGA.LE.OMEGA2) THEN
         MAG = ABS((A*CMPLX(OMEGA)**2 + B*CMPLX(OMEGA) + C)
     +              /(CMPLX(OMEGA)**2 + D*CMPLX(OMEGA) + E))
         PRINT 15, OMEGA, MAG
   15    FORMAT(1X, F5.1, 12X, F9.4)
         OMEGA = OMEGA + INTRVL
         GO TO 10
      ENDIF
*
      END
*----------------------------------------------------------------*
```

22.
```
*----------------------------------------------------------------*
      PROGRAM MAGNTD
*
*   This program computes and prints the magnitude  effects
*   for a requested number of frequency points.
*
      REAL  MAG, OMEGA1, OMEGA2, OMEGA, INTRVL
      INTEGER  NUMBER
      COMPLEX  A, B, C, D, E
*
      PRINT*, 'ENTER THE COEFFICIENTS, A, B, C, D, E...'
      READ*, A, B, C, D, E
      PRINT*, 'ENTER THE BEGINING AND ENDING FREQUENCIES'
      READ*, OMEGA1, OMEGA2
      PRINT*, 'ENTER THE THE NUMBER OF POINTS FOR THE INTERVAL'
      READ*, NUMBER
*
      PRINT*, 'MAGNITUDE EFFECTS FOR', NUMBER, ' FREQUENCY POINTS'
      PRINT*, 'OMEGA              MAGNITUDE'
*
      INTRVL = (ABS(OMEGA2 - OMEGA1)+1.0)/REAL(NUMBER)
      OMEGA = OMEGA1
*
   10 IF (OMEGA.LE.OMEGA2) THEN
```

```
            MAG = ABS((A*CMPLX(OMEGA)**2 + B*CMPLX(OMEGA) + C)
     +                /(CMPLX(OMEGA)**2 + D*CMPLX(OMEGA) + E))
            PRINT 15, OMEGA, MAG
     15     FORMAT(1X, F5.1, 12X, F9.4)
            OMEGA = OMEGA + INTRVL
            GO TO 10
         ENDIF
*
         END
*------------------------------------------------------------*
```

23.
```
*------------------------------------------------------------*
         PROGRAM CMPEXP
*
*  This program compares exp(x) computed using the single
*  precision intrinsic function to exp(x) computed using the
*  double precision intrinsic function.
*
         INTEGER  I
         REAL  X
         DOUBLE PRECISION  DX
*
         PRINT 5
       5 FORMAT('1', 15X, 'EXP(X) COMPARISON'//
     +          1X, ' X ', 5X, 'SINGLE PRECISION',
     +          1X, 5X, 'DOUBLE PRECISION')
         DO 10 I = 1, 20
            X = REAL(I)*0.1
            DX = DBLE(I)*0.1D+00
            PRINT 15, X, EXP(X), DEXP(DX)
     15     FORMAT(1X, F3.1, 5X, F15.12, 7X, F15.12)
     10 CONTINUE
*
         END
*------------------------------------------------------------*
```

24.
```
*------------------------------------------------------------*
         SUBROUTINE DELETE(TEXT, PTR)
*
*  This subroutine deletes the character pointed
*  to in TEXT by PTR.
*
         INTEGER  I, PTR
         CHARACTER*100  TEXT
'*
         DO 10 I = PTR, 99
            TEXT(I:I) = TEXT(I+1:I+1)
     10 CONTINUE
*
         TEXT(100:100) = ' '
*
         RETURN
         END
*------------------------------------------------------------*
```

203

```
25.   *----------------------------------------------------------------*
          SUBROUTINE  INSERT(TEXT, PTR, CHAR1)
      *
      *   This subroutine inserts a character in the position
      *   pointed to in TEXT by PTR.
      *
          INTEGER  I, PTR
          CHARACTER*100  TEXT
          CHARACTER*1  CHAR1
      *
          DO 10 I = 100, PTR+1, -1
              TEXT(I:I) = TEXT(I-1:I-1)
       10 CONTINUE
      *
          TEXT(PTR:PTR) = CHAR1
      *
          RETURN
          END
      *----------------------------------------------------------------*


26.   *----------------------------------------------------------------*
          PROGRAM  RATION
      *
      *   This program prints a report to be used to
      *   study the feasibility of gas rationing.
      *
          INTEGER  I
          REAL  SUMODD, SUMEVN, SUM, PERCO, PERCE, GALNS
          LOGICAL  ODD
          CHARACTER*7  PLATE
      *   CHARACTER*3  LETTER, NUMBER
          CHARACTER*1  CH(5)
          DATA  CH/'0', '2', '4', '6', '8'/
      *
          OPEN(UNIT=9, FILE='CARS', STATUS='OLD')
      *
          SUMODD = 0.0
          SUMEVN = 0.0
      *
          READ(9,5) PLATE, GALNS
        5 FORMAT(A, 1X, F5.3)
      *
       15 IF (PLATE.NE.'ZZZ 999') THEN
              ODD = .TRUE.
              DO 10 I = 1, 5
                  IF (PLATE(6:6).EQ.CH(I)) ODD = .FALSE.
       10     CONTINUE
              IF (ODD) THEN
                  SUMODD = SUMODD + GALNS
              ELSE
                  SUMEVN = SUMEVN + GALNS
              ENDIF
              READ(9,20) PLATE, GALNS
       20     FORMAT(A, 1X, F5.3)
              GO TO 15
```

```
          ENDIF
*
          SUM = SUMODD + SUMEVN
          PERCO = SUMODD/SUM*100.0
          PERCE = SUMEVN/SUM*100.0
*
          PRINT 25, INT(SUMODD), PERCO
       25 FORMAT(1X, 'SUM OF GAS FOR ODD CARS', 4X, I5,
          +        ' GALLONS ', 4X, F4.1, '%')
          PRINT 30, INT(SUMEVN), PERCE
       30 FORMAT(1X, 'SUM OF GAS FOR EVEN CARS', 3X, I5,
          +        ' GALLONS ', 4X, F4.1, '%')
*
          END
*-------------------------------------------------------------*
```

27.
```
*-------------------------------------------------------------*
          LOGICAL FUNCTION PALIND(X)
*
*  This function returns a value of TRUE if X is a
*  palindrome and a value of FALSE otherwise.
*
          INTEGER  I, J
          CHARACTER*(*)  X
*
          N = LEN(X)
          PALIND = .TRUE.
*
          DO 10 I = 1, N/2
             J = N - (I-1)
             IF (X(I:I).NE.X(J:J)) PALIND = .FALSE.
       10 CONTINUE
*
          RETURN
          END
*-------------------------------------------------------------*
```

28.
```
*-------------------------------------------------------------*
          SUBROUTINE  ALPHA(LETTRS)
*
*  This subroutine sorts the array  NAME into
*  alphabetical order.
*
          INTEGER  I, J
          CHARACTER*1  LETTRS(50), HOLD
*
*
          DO 20 I = 1, 49
             DO 10 J = 1, 49
                IF (LETTRS(J).GT.LETTRS(J+1)) THEN
                   HOLD = LETTRS(J)
                   LETTRS(J) = LETTRS(J+1)
                   LETTRS(J+1) = HOLD
                ENDIF
       10    CONTINUE
```

```
      20 CONTINUE
   *
         RETURN
         END
   *------------------------------------------------------------*

29.   *------------------------------------------------------------*
         SUBROUTINE REMDUP(LETTRS)
   *
   *  This subroutine removes any duplicate letters in the
   *  array LETTRS and adds blanks at the end of the array
   *  for the removed letters.
   *
         INTEGER  I, J, K
         CHARACTER*1  LETTRS(50)
   *
         DO 30 I = 1, 49
            DO 20 J = I+1, 50
               IF (LETTRS(I).EQ.LETTRS(J)) THEN
                  DO 10 K = J, 49
                     LETTRS(K) = LETTRS(K+1)
      10            CONTINUE
                  LETTRS(50) = ' '
               ENDIF
      20     CONTINUE
      30 CONTINUE
   *
         RETURN
         END
   *------------------------------------------------------------*

30.   *------------------------------------------------------------*
         SUBROUTINE  EDIT(STRING)
   *
   *  This subroutine changes all punctuation
   *  characters in STRING to blanks.
   *
         INTEGER  I, J
         CHARACTER*50  STRING
         CHARACTER*4  PUNCT
   *
         PUNCT = ',.!?'
   *
         DO 20 I = 1, 50
            DO 10 J = 1, 4
               IF (STRING(I:I).EQ.PUNCT(J:J))  STRING(I:I) = ' '
      10     CONTINUE
      20 CONTINUE
   *
         RETURN
         END
   *------------------------------------------------------------*

31.   *------------------------------------------------------------*
         SUBROUTINE  TEXT(PROSE)
```

```
*
*   This subroutine breaks PROSE into lines of
*   no more than 30 characters.
*
      INTEGER  END, START
      CHARACTER*200 PROSE
*
      START = 1
      END = 30
*
    1 IF (END.LT.200) THEN
          IF (PROSE(END+1:END+1).EQ.' ') THEN
              IF(PROSE(START:END).NE.' ')PRINT 5,PROSE(START:END)
    5         FORMAT(1X, A)
              START = END + 2
              END = START + 29
          ELSE
              END = END - 1
              IF (END.EQ.START) PRINT 8
    8             FORMAT(1X, 'WORD LONGER THAN 30 CHARACTERS')
          ENDIF
          GO TO 1
      ENDIF
*
      IF (PROSE(START:).NE.' ') PRINT 5, PROSE(START:)
*
      RETURN
      END
*------------------------------------------------------------*
```

32.
```
*------------------------------------------------------------*
      INTEGER FUNCTION  CONSNT(CHAR)
*
*   This function counts the number of consonants in an
*   array of character strings.
*
      INTEGER  I, J, CONSNT
      CHARACTER*1  CHAR(100)
      CHARACTER*5  VOWEL
*
      VOWEL = 'AEIOU'
      CONSNT = 100
*
      DO 10 I = 1, 100
         DO 5 J = 1, 5
             IF (CHAR(I).EQ.VOWEL(J:J))  CONSNT = CONSNT - 1
    5    CONTINUE
   10 CONTINUE
*
      RETURN
      END
*------------------------------------------------------------*
```

33.
```
*------------------------------------------------------------*
      SUBROUTINE  PLOT(DATA, N)
```

```
*
*   This subroutine generates a printer plot
*   of data in an array.
*
      INTEGER  N, I, K
      REAL  DATA(N), AMAX
      CHARACTER*101  AXIS, LINE
*
      DO 5 I = 1, 101
         AXIS(I:I) = '.'
         LINE(I:I) = ' '
    5 CONTINUE
*
      AMAX = ABS(DATA(1))
      DO 20 I = 2, N
         IF (ABS(DATA(I)).GT.AMAX)  AMAX = ABS(DATA(I))
   20 CONTINUE
      PRINT*, 'AMAX = ', AMAX
*
      PRINT*, AXIS
*
      DO 30 I = 1, N
         LINE(51:51) = '.'
         K = (DATA(I) + AMAX)/(2.0*AMAX)*100.0 + 1.0
         LINE(K:K) = 'X'
         PRINT*, LINE
         LINE(K:K) = ' '
   30 CONTINUE
*
      RETURN
      END
*-----------------------------------------------------------*
```

34.
```
      *-----------------------------------------------------------*
      PROGRAM  HIDDEN
*
*   This program searches a character array
*   for hidden words.
*
      INTEGER  I, J, NHID, LEN
      CHARACTER*6  WORDS(9), HID
*
      DO 10 I = 1, 9
         READ(5,1) WORDS(I)
   10 CONTINUE
*
      DO 50 NHID = 1, 11
*
            READ(5,1) HID
    1    FORMAT(A)
*
         J = 6
   20    IF (HID(J:J).EQ.' ') THEN
            J = J - 1
            GO TO 20
```

208

```
            ENDIF
            LEN = J
*
            DO 30 I = 1, 9
                DO 25 J = 1, 6
                    IF (HID(1:1).EQ.WORDS(I)(J:J))
     +                  CALL SEARCH(WORDS, HID, LEN, I, J)
   25           CONTINUE
   30       CONTINUE
*
   50 CONTINUE
*
      END
*-------------------------------------------------------------*
      SUBROUTINE  SEARCH(WORDS, HID, LEN, I, J)
*
* This subroutine looks for the hidden words.
*
      INTEGER  IDIR(8), JDIR(8), I, J, K, N, LEN, M, L,
     +         ISIGN
      LOGICAL  FOUND
      CHARACTER*6  WORDS(9), HID
*
      DATA  IDIR, JDIR/0, 3*-1, 0, 5*1, 0, 3*-1, 0, 1/
*
      N = 1
   40 IF (N.LE.8) THEN
          IF (((J + JDIR(N)*LEN).LE.7).AND.
     +        ((J + JDIR(N)*LEN).GE.0)) THEN
              IF (((I + IDIR(N)*LEN).LE.10).AND.
     +            ((I + IDIR(N)*LEN).GE.0)) THEN
              M = 1
              FOUND = .TRUE.
   10         IF (M.LE.LEN) THEN
                  K = J + M*JDIR(N) - JDIR(N)
                  L = I + M*IDIR(N) - IDIR(N)
                  ISIGN = (-1*N)**N
                  IF ((HID(M:M).EQ.WORDS(I)(K:K).AND.ISIGN.LT.0)
     +            .OR.(HID(M:M).EQ.WORDS(L)(K:K).AND.ISIGN.GT.0)
     +            .OR.(JDIR(N).EQ.0.AND.HID(M:M).EQ.WORDS(L)(K:K)))
     +            THEN
                      M = M + 1
                  ELSE
                      M = LEN + 1
                      FOUND = .FALSE.
                  ENDIF
                  GO TO 10
              ENDIF
              IF ((M.GT.LEN).AND.(FOUND)) THEN
                  DO 30 M = 1, LEN
                      K = J + M*JDIR(N) - JDIR(N)
                      L = I + M*IDIR(N) - IDIR(N)
                      IF (IDIR(N).EQ.0) THEN
                          PRINT 20, I, K
                      ELSEIF (JDIR(N).EQ.0) THEN
```

```
                                    PRINT 20, L, J
                            ELSEIF(IDIR(N).NE.0.AND.JDIR(N).NE.0)THEN
                                PRINT 20, L, K
                            ENDIF
      20                    FORMAT (1X, I3, ':', I3)
      30              CONTINUE
                  ENDIF
              ENDIF
          ENDIF
          N = N + 1
          GO TO 40
      ENDIF
*
      RETURN
      END
*------------------------------------------------------------*
```

35.
```
*------------------------------------------------------------*
      SUBROUTINE   TEXT(PROSE, LINE)
*
*  This subroutine breaks PROSE into lines of
*  characters with blanks evenly distributed.
*
      INTEGER  END, START, LINE
      CHARACTER*200  PROSE
*
      START = 1
      END = LINE
*
    1 IF ((END.LT.200).AND.(END.GE.1)) THEN
          IF (PROSE(END+1:END+1).EQ.' ')  THEN
             IF (PROSE(START:END).NE.' ')
     +          CALL DIST(PROSE(START:END), LINE)
             START = END + 2
             END = START + LINE - 1
          ELSE
             END = END - 1
             IF (END.EQ.START) PRINT 8
    8        FORMAT(1X, 'WORD LONGER THAN LINE')
          ENDIF
          GO TO 1
      ENDIF
*
      IF (PROSE(START:).NE.' ')CALL DIST (PROSE(START:), LINE)
*
      RETURN
      END
*------------------------------------------------------------*
      SUBROUTINE   DIST(INPUT, LINE)
*
*  This subroutine distributes beginning and ending
*  blanks within a string and print the resultant string.
*
      INTEGER  BLKS, K, N, I, LINE
      CHARACTER*(*)  INPUT
```

210

```fortran
      CHARACTER*200  TEMP, STRING
*
      STRING = INPUT
      K = 1
  10  IF (STRING(K:K).EQ.' ') THEN
          K = K + 1
          GO TO 10
      ENDIF
      TEMP = STRING(K:)
      STRING = TEMP
*
      BLKS = 0
      K = LINE
  20  IF (STRING(K:K).EQ.' ') THEN
          BLKS = BLKS + 1
          K = K - 1
        GO TO 20
      ENDIF
*
      K = LINE
      N = INDEX(STRING, ' ')
      IF ((BLKS.EQ.0).OR.((N + BLKS - 1).EQ.K)) THEN
          PRINT 55, STRING(:LINE)
      ELSE
  40     IF (BLKS.NE.0) THEN
            I = 1
  50        IF (I.LE.K-1) THEN
                IF (BLKS.NE.0) THEN
              IF ((STRING(I:I).EQ.' ').AND.
     +            (STRING(I+1:I+1).NE.' ')) THEN
                    TEMP = STRING(:I)//' '//STRING(I+1:)
                    STRING = TEMP
                    BLKS = BLKS - 1
                    I = I + 1
                  ENDIF
                ENDIF
                I = I + 1
                GO TO 50
            ENDIF
            GO TO 40
         ENDIF
*
         PRINT 55, STRING(:LINE)
  55     FORMAT(1X, A)
*
      ENDIF
*
      RETURN
      END
*----------------------------------------------------------*
```

```fortran
*----------------------------------------------------------*
      REAL FUNCTION  WORDAV(TEXT)
*
* This function computes the average word
```

```
*   length of the character string TEXT.
*
      INTEGER  I, J, N, K, FIRST, NWORDS, NLETRS, NEXTBL,
     +         LETRS
      CHARACTER*(*) TEXT
      CHARACTER*6  PUNCT
*
      PUNCT = '.,;:!?'
      NWORDS = 0
      NLETRS = 0
      FIRST = 1
      N = LEN(TEXT)
*
   10 IF (FIRST.LE.N) THEN
         IF (TEXT(FIRST:FIRST).NE.' ') THEN
            NEXTBL = INDEX(TEXT(FIRST:N), ' ')
            IF (NEXTBL.EQ.0)  NEXTBL = N - FIRST + 2
            LETRS = NEXTBL - 1
            K = FIRST + LETRS - 1
            DO 15 I = FIRST, K
               DO 12 J = 1, 6
                  IF (TEXT(I:I).EQ.PUNCT(J:J)) LETRS=LETRS-1
   12          CONTINUE
   15       CONTINUE
            NLETRS = NLETRS + LETRS
            NWORDS = NWORDS + 1
            FIRST = NEXTBL +  FIRST - 1
         ELSE
            FIRST = FIRST + 1
         ENDIF
         GO TO 10
      ENDIF
*
      IF (NLETRS.EQ.0) THEN
         WORDAV = 0.0
      ELSE
         WORDAV = NLETRS/REAL(NWORDS)
      ENDIF
*
      RETURN
      END
*------------------------------------------------------------*

37.  *------------------------------------------------------------*
      SUBROUTINE  ORDER(CDATA, N)
*
*   This subroutine sorts a complex array into
*   descending order.
*
      INTEGER  I, J, N
      COMPLEX  CDATA(N), CTEMP
*
      DO 20 I = 1, N-1
         DO 10 J = 1, N-1
            IF (ABS(CDATA(J+1)).LT.ABS(CDATA(J))) THEN
```

```
                CTEMP = CDATA(J)
                CDATA(J) = CDATA(J+1)
                CDATA(J+1) = CTEMP
             ENDIF
   10    CONTINUE
   20 CONTINUE
*
      RETURN
      END
*------------------------------------------------------------*
```

38.
```
*------------------------------------------------------------*
      SUBROUTINE  ENCODE(KEY, MESSGE, SECRET)
*
*  This subroutine encodes a message.
*
      INTEGER  I, J, LENGTH
      CHARACTER*26  KEY, ALPHA
      CHARACTER*(*)  MESSGE, SECRET
*
      DATA  ALPHA /'ABCDEFGHIJKLMNOPQRSTUVWXYZ'/
*
      LENGTH = LEN(MESSGE)
*
      DO 20 I = 1, LENGTH
         J = 1
   15    IF ((MESSGE(I:I).NE.ALPHA(J:J)).AND.(J.LT.26)) THEN
            J = J + 1
            GO TO 15
         ENDIF
         IF (MESSGE(I:I).EQ.ALPHA(J:J)) THEN
            SECRET(I:I) = KEY(J:J)
         ELSE
            SECRET(I:I) = MESSGE(I:I)
         ENDIF
   20 CONTINUE
*
      RETURN
      END
*------------------------------------------------------------*
```

39.
```
*------------------------------------------------------------*
      SUBROUTINE  DECODE(KEY, SECRET, MESSGE)
*
*  This subroutine decodes a secret message.
*
      INTEGER  I, J, LENGTH
      CHARACTER*26  KEY, ALPHA
      CHARACTER*(*)  MESSGE, SECRET
*
      DATA  ALPHA /'ABCDEFGHIJKLMNOPQRSTUVWXYZ'/
*
      LENGTH = LEN(MESSGE)
*
      DO 20 I = 1, LENGTH
```

```
            J = 1
    15      IF ((SECRET(I:I).NE.KEY(J:J)).AND.(J.LT.26)) THEN
               J = J + 1
               GO TO 15
            ENDIF
            IF (SECRET(I:I).EQ.KEY(J:J)) THEN
               MESSGE(I:I) = ALPHA(J:J)
            ELSE
               MESSGE(I:I) = SECRET(I:I)
            ENDIF
    20 CONTINUE
*
       RETURN
       END
*------------------------------------------------------------*


40.    *------------------------------------------------------------*
       SUBROUTINE   ALPHA(NAME, N)
*
*  This subroutine alphabetizes the array NAME.
*
       INTEGER  N, I, J
       CHARACTER*4  NAME(N), HOLD
*
       DO 10 I = 1, N
          J = 1
     5    IF ((NAME(I)(J:J).EQ.' ').AND.(J.LT.4)) THEN
             J = J + 1
             GO TO 5
          ENDIF
          NAME(I) = NAME(I)(J:)
    10 CONTINUE
*
       DO 20 I = 1, N-1
          DO 15 J = 1, N-1
             IF (NAME(J).GT.NAME(J+1)) THEN
                HOLD = NAME(J)
                NAME(J) = NAME(J+1)
                NAME(J+1) = HOLD
             ENDIF
    15    CONTINUE
    20 CONTINUE
*
       RETURN
       END
*------------------------------------------------------------*
```

```
1.   *------------------------------------------------------------*
        PROGRAM  MIGRAT
     *
     * This program merges new sighting information into the
     * master file of migration information on whooping cranes.
     *
        INTEGER  M,D,Y,T,MO,DA,YR,TIME,GRID1,GRID2,BIRDS,
       +         SMO,SDA,SYR,STIME,SGRID1,SGRID2,SBIRDS,
       +         CMO,CDA,CYR,CTIME,CGRID1,CGRID2,CBIRDS,COUNT
        DOUBLE PRECISION  DATE, CDATE, SDATE
        LOGICAL  DONE
     *
        DATE(M,D,Y,T) = DBLE(REAL(Y)*1.0D08) +
       +                DBLE(REAL(M)*1.0D06) +
       +                DBLE(REAL(D)*1.0D04) +
       +                DBLE(REAL(T))
     *
        OPEN (UNIT=10,FILE='SIGHTS',STATUS='OLD')
        OPEN (UNIT=11,FILE='CRANES',STATUS='OLD')
        OPEN (UNIT=12,FILE='TEMP',STATUS='NEW')
     *
        READ (10,5) SMO,SDA,SYR,STIME,SGRID1,SGRID2,SBIRDS
      5 FORMAT (3I2,1X,I4,1X,2I2,1X,I4)
        READ (11,5) CMO,CDA,CYR,CTIME,CGRID1,CGRID2,CBIRDS
        SDATE = DATE(SMO,SDA,SYR,STIME)
        CDATE = DATE(CMO,CDA,CYR,CTIME)
        IF (SMO.EQ.99.AND.CMO.EQ.99) THEN
            DONE = .TRUE.
        ELSE
            DONE = .FALSE.
        ENDIF
     *
     10 IF (.NOT.DONE) THEN
            IF (CDATE.LT.SDATE) THEN
                WRITE (12,5) CMO,CDA,CYR,CTIME,CGRID1,
       +                     CGRID2,CBIRDS
                READ (11,5) CMO,CDA,CYR,CTIME,CGRID1,
       +                    CGRID2,CBIRDS
                CDATE = DATE(CMO,CDA,CYR,CTIME)
            ELSE
                WRITE (12,5) SMO,SDA,SYR,STIME,SGRID1,
       +                     SGRID2,SBIRDS
                READ (10,5) SMO,SDA,SYR,STIME,SGRID1,
       +                    SGRID2,SBIRDS
                SDATE = DATE(SMO,SDA,SYR,STIME)
            ENDIF
            IF (SMO.EQ.99.AND.CMO.EQ.99) DONE = .TRUE.
            GO TO 10
        ENDIF
        WRITE (12,5) SMO,SDA,SYR,STIME,SGRID1,SGRID2,SBIRDS
        CLOSE (UNIT=11,STATUS='DELETE')
        CLOSE (UNIT=12)
     *
```

```
            OPEN (UNIT=11,FILE='CRANES', STATUS='NEW')
            OPEN (UNIT=12,FILE='TEMP', STATUS='OLD')
            PRINT*, 'WHOOPING CRANE MIGRATION'
            PRINT*
            PRINT*, 'CURRENT SIGHTINGS'
            PRINT*
      *
            COUNT = 0
      15 READ (12,5,END=32) MO,DA,YR,TIME,GRID1,GRID2,BIRDS
            IF (MO.NE.99) THEN
                PRINT 20, MO,DA,YR,TIME
      20        FORMAT (1X,I2,'-',I2,'-',I2,4X,I4)
                PRINT 25, GRID1,GRID2
      25        FORMAT (1X,5X,'GRID LOCATION: ',2I3)
                PRINT 30, BIRDS
      30        FORMAT (1X,5X,'NUMBER OF BIRDS',1X,I5)
                COUNT = COUNT + 1
            ENDIF
            WRITE (11,5) MO,DA,YR,TIME,GRID1,GRID2,BIRDS
            GO TO 15
      32 PRINT 35, COUNT
      35 FORMAT (1X,'TOTAL NUMBER OF SIGHTINGS = ',I4)
      *
      50 STOP
         END
      *-----------------------------------------------------------*


2.    *-----------------------------------------------------------*
         PROGRAM  MIGRAT
      *
      * This program merges new sighting information into the
      * master file of migration information on whooping cranes.
      *  .
         INTEGER   M,D,Y,T,MO,DA,YR,TIME,GRID1,GRID2,BIRDS,
       +           SMO,SDA,SYR,STIME,SGRID1,SGRID2,SBIRDS,
       +           CMO,CDA,CYR,CTIME,CGRID1,CGRID2,CBIRDS,MAX
         DOUBLE PRECISION  DATE, CDATE, SDATE
         LOGICAL  DONE
      *
         DATE(M,D,Y,T) = DBLE(REAL(Y)*1.0D08) +
       +                 DBLE(REAL(M)*1.0D06) +
       +                 DBLE(REAL(D)*1.0D04) +
       +                 DBLE(REAL(T))
      *
         OPEN (UNIT=10,FILE='SIGHTS',STATUS='OLD')
         OPEN (UNIT=11,FILE='CRANES',STATUS='OLD')
         OPEN (UNIT=12,FILE='TEMP',STATUS='NEW')
      *
         READ (10,5) SMO,SDA,SYR,STIME,SGRID1,SGRID2,SBIRDS
       5 FORMAT (3I2,1X,I4,1X,2I2,1X,I4)
         READ (11,5) CMO,CDA,CYR,CTIME,CGRID1,CGRID2,CBIRDS
         SDATE = DATE(SMO,SDA,SYR,STIME)
         CDATE = DATE(CMO,CDA,CYR,CTIME)
         IF (SMO.EQ.99.AND.CMO.EQ.99) THEN
            DONE = .TRUE.
```

```
         ELSE
            DONE = .FALSE.
         ENDIF
*
    10 IF (.NOT.DONE) THEN
         IF (CDATE.LT.SDATE) THEN
            WRITE (12,5) CMO,CDA,CYR,CTIME,CGRID1,
    +                    CGRID2,CBIRDS
            READ (11,5) CMO,CDA,CYR,CTIME,CGRID1,
    +                   CGRID2,CBIRDS
            CDATE = DATE(CMO,CDA,CYR,CTIME)
         ELSE
            WRITE (12,5) SMO,SDA,SYR,STIME,SGRID1,
    +                    SGRID2,SBIRDS
            READ (10,5) SMO,SDA,SYR,STIME,SGRID1,
    +                   SGRID2,SBIRDS
            SDATE = DATE(SMO,SDA,SYR,STIME)
         ENDIF
         IF (SMO.EQ.99.AND.CMO.EQ.99) DONE = .TRUE.
         GO TO 10
       ENDIF
       WRITE (12,5) SMO,SDA,SYR,STIME,SGRID1,SGRID2,SBIRDS
       CLOSE (UNIT=11,STATUS='DELETE')
       CLOSE (UNIT=12)
*
       OPEN (UNIT=11,FILE='CRANES', STATUS='NEW')
       OPEN (UNIT=12,FILE='TEMP', STATUS='OLD')
       PRINT*, 'WHOOPING CRANE MIGRATION'
       PRINT*
       PRINT*, 'CURRENT SIGHTINGS'
       PRINT*
*
       MAX = 0
    15 READ (12,5,END=32) MO,DA,YR,TIME,GRID1,GRID2,BIRDS
         IF (MO.NE.99) THEN
            IF (BIRDS.GT.MAX) MAX = BIRDS
            PRINT 20, MO,DA,YR,TIME
    20      FORMAT (1X,I2,'-',I2,'-',I2,4X,I4)
            PRINT 25, GRID1,GRID2
    25      FORMAT (1X,5X,'GRID LOCATION: ',2I3)
            PRINT 30, BIRDS
    30      FORMAT (1X,5X,'NUMBER OF BIRDS',1X,I5)
         ENDIF
         WRITE (11,5) MO,DA,YR,TIME,GRID1,GRID2,BIRDS
         GO TO 15
    32 CONTINUE
*
    50 PRINT 60, MAX
    60 FORMAT(1X,/,'THE MAXIMUM NUMBER OF BIRDS SIGHTED WAS '
    +         I5)
*
       END
*-----------------------------------------------------------*

3.  *-----------------------------------------------------------*
```

```
      PROGRAM  MIGRAT
*
*  This program merges new sighting information into the
*  master file of migration information on whooping cranes.
*
      INTEGER  M,D,Y,T,MO,DA,YR,TIME,GRID1,GRID2,BIRDS,
     +         SMO,SDA,SYR,STIME,SGRID1,SGRID2,SBIRDS,
     + CMO,CDA,CYR,CTIME,CGRID1,CGRID2,CBIRDS,
     +         GRID(100,2)
      DOUBLE PRECISION  DATE, CDATE, SDATE
      LOGICAL  DONE
      DATA  GRID /200*0/
*
      DATE(M,D,Y,T) = DBLE(REAL(Y)*1.0D08) +
     +                DBLE(REAL(M)*1.0D06) +
     +                DBLE(REAL(D)*1.0D04) +
     +                DBLE(REAL(T))
*
      OPEN (UNIT=10,FILE='SIGHTS',STATUS='OLD')
      OPEN (UNIT=11,FILE='CRANES',STATUS='OLD')
      OPEN (UNIT=12,FILE='TEMP',STATUS='NEW')
*
      READ (10,5) SMO,SDA,SYR,STIME,SGRID1,SGRID2,SBIRDS
    5 FORMAT (3I2,1X,I4,1X,2I2,1X,I4)
      READ (11,5) CMO,CDA,CYR,CTIME,CGRID1,CGRID2,CBIRDS
      SDATE = DATE(SMO,SDA,SYR,STIME)
      CDATE = DATE(CMO,CDA,CYR,CTIME)
      IF (SMO.EQ.99.AND.CMO.EQ.99) THEN
         DONE = .TRUE.
      ELSE
         DONE = .FALSE.
      ENDIF
*
   10 IF (.NOT.DONE) THEN
         IF (CDATE.LT.SDATE) THEN
            WRITE (12,5) CMO,CDA,CYR,CTIME,CGRID1,
     +                   CGRID2,CBIRDS
            READ (11,5) CMO,CDA,CYR,CTIME,CGRID1,
     +                   CGRID2,CBIRDS
            CDATE = DATE(CMO,CDA,CYR,CTIME)
         ELSE
            WRITE (12,5) SMO,SDA,SYR,STIME,SGRID1,
     +                   SGRID2,SBIRDS
            READ (10,5) SMO,SDA,SYR,STIME,SGRID1,
     +                   SGRID2,SBIRDS
            SDATE = DATE(SMO,SDA,SYR,STIME)
         ENDIF
         IF (SMO.EQ.99.AND.CMO.EQ.99)  DONE = .TRUE.
         GO TO 10
      ENDIF
      WRITE (12,5) SMO,SDA,SYR,STIME,SGRID1,SGRID2,SBIRDS
      CLOSE (UNIT=11,STATUS='DELETE')
      CLOSE (UNIT=12)
*
      OPEN (UNIT=11,FILE='CRANES',STATUS='NEW')
```

```
      OPEN (UNIT=12,FILE='TEMP',STATUS='OLD')
      PRINT*, 'WHOOPING CRANE MIGRATION'
      PRINT*
      PRINT*, 'CURRENT SIGHTINGS'
      PRINT*
*
   15 READ (12,5,END=50) MO,DA,YR,TIME,GRID1,GRID2,BIRDS
         IF (MO.NE.99) THEN
            PRINT 20, MO,DA,YR,TIME
   20       FORMAT (1X,I2,'-',I2,'-',I2,4X,I4)
            PRINT 25, GRID1,GRID2
   25       FORMAT (1X,5X,'GRID LOCATION: ',2I3)
            PRINT 30, BIRDS
   30       FORMAT (1X,5X,'NUMBER OF BIRDS',1X,I5)
            CALL GRIDCK(GRID1,GRID2,GRID)
         ENDIF
         WRITE (11,5) MO,DA,YR,TIME,GRID1,GRID2,BIRDS
         GO TO 15
      CALL GRIDPR(GRID)
*
   50 STOP
      END
*------------------------------------------------------------*
      SUBROUTINE  GRIDCK(GRID1,GRID2,GRID)
*
* This subroutine keeps track of the sightings
* in individual grids.
*
      INTEGER  GRID1, GRID2, GRID(100,2), CODE, I
      LOGICAL  DONE
*
      CODE = GRID1*100 + GRID2
      I = 1
      DONE = .FALSE.
    5 IF (.NOT.DONE) THEN
         IF (GRID(I,1).EQ.0.OR.GRID(I,1).EQ.CODE
     +      .OR.I.EQ.100) THEN
            DONE = .TRUE.
         ELSE
            I = I + 1
         ENDIF
         GO TO 5
      ENDIF
      IF (GRID(I,1).EQ.0) THEN
         GRID(I,1) = CODE
         GRID(I,2) = 1
      ELSEIF (GRID(I,1).EQ.CODE) THEN
         GRID(I,2) = GRID(I,2) + 1
      ELSE
         PRINT*, 'GRID ARRAY TOO SMALL'
      ENDIF
*
      RETURN
      END
*------------------------------------------------------------*
```

```
      SUBROUTINE  GRIDPR(GRID)
*
*  This subroutine prints the sightings in individual grids.
*
      INTEGER  GRID(100,2), GRID1, GRID2
*
      PRINT*, 'SIGHTNGS BY GRID LOCATION'
      PRINT*, ' GRID   NUMBER OF SIGHTINGS'
      I = 1
   10 IF (GRID(I,1).NE.0.AND.I.LE.100) THEN
         GRID2 = MOD(GRID(I,1),100)
         GRID1 = GRID(I,1)/100
         PRINT 20, GRID1, GRID2, GRID(I,2)
   20    FORMAT (1X,I2,1X,I2,5X,I4)
         I = I + 1
         GO TO 10
      ENDIF
*
      RETURN
      END
*------------------------------------------------------------*
```

4.
```
*------------------------------------------------------------*
      PROGRAM  MIGRAT
*
*  This program merges new sighting information into the
*  master file of migration information on whooping cranes.
*
      INTEGER  M,D,Y,T,MO,DA,YR,TIME,GRID1,GRID2,BIRDS,
     +         SMO,SDA,SYR,STIME,SGRID1,SGRID2,SBIRDS,
     +         CMO,CDA,CYR,CTIME,CGRID1,CGRID2,CBIRDS,SIZE
      DOUBLE PRECISION  DATE, CDATE, SDATE
      LOGICAL  DONE
*
      DATE(M,D,Y,T) = DBLE(REAL(Y)*1.0D08) +
     +                DBLE(REAL(M)*1.0D06) +
     +                DBLE(REAL(D)*1.0D04) +
     +                DBLE(REAL(T))
*
      OPEN (UNIT=10,FILE='SIGHTS',STATUS='OLD')
      OPEN (UNIT=11,FILE='CRANES',STATUS='OLD')
      OPEN (UNIT=12,FILE='TEMP',STATUS='NEW')
*
      PRINT*, 'ENTER THE SIGHTING SIZE OF INTEREST: '
      READ*, SIZE
*
      READ (10,5) SMO,SDA,SYR,STIME,SGRID1,SGRID2,SBIRDS
    5 FORMAT (3I2,1X,I4,1X,2I2,1X,I4)
      READ (11,5) CMO,CDA,CYR,CTIME,CGRID1,CGRID2,CBIRDS
      SDATE = DATE(SMO,SDA,SYR,STIME)
      CDATE = DATE(CMO,CDA,CYR,CTIME)
      IF (SMO.EQ.99.AND.CMO.EQ.99) THEN
         DONE = .TRUE.
      ELSE
         DONE = .FALSE.
```

```
            ENDIF
      *
         10 IF (.NOT.DONE) THEN
               IF (CDATE.LT.SDATE) THEN
                   WRITE (12,5) CMO,CDA,CYR,CTIME,CGRID1,
              +                  CGRID2,CBIRDS
                   READ (11,5) CMO,CDA,CYR,CTIME,CGRID1,
              +                 CGRID2,CBIRDS
                   CDATE = DATE(CMO,CDA,CYR,CTIME)
               ELSE
                   WRITE (12,5) SMO,SDA,SYR,STIME,SGRID1,
              +                  SGRID2,SBIRDS
                   READ (10,5) SMO,SDA,SYR,STIME,SGRID1,
              +                 SGRID2,SBIRDS
                   SDATE = DATE(SMO,SDA,SYR,STIME)
               ENDIF
               IF (SMO.EQ.99.AND.CMO.EQ.99) DONE = .TRUE.
               GO TO 10
            ENDIF
            WRITE (12,5) SMO,SDA,SYR,STIME,SGRID1,SGRID2,SBIRDS
            CLOSE (UNIT=11,STATUS='DELETE')
            CLOSE (UNIT=12)
      *
            OPEN (UNIT=11,FILE='CRANES', STATUS='NEW')
            OPEN (UNIT=12,FILE='TEMP', STATUS='OLD')
            PRINT*, 'WHOOPING CRANE MIGRATION'
            PRINT*
            PRINT*, 'CURRENT SIGHTINGS OF SIZE ',SIZE
            PRINT*
      *
         15 READ (12,5,END=32) MO,DA,YR,TIME,GRID1,GRID2,BIRDS
               IF (MO.NE.99.AND.BIRDS.EQ.SIZE) THEN
                   PRINT 20, MO,DA,YR,TIME
         20        FORMAT (1X,I2,'-',I2,'-',I2,4X,I4)
                   PRINT 25, GRID1,GRID2
         25        FORMAT (1X,5X,'GRID LOCATION: ',2I3)
                   PRINT 30, BIRDS
         30        FORMAT (1X,5X,'NUMBER OF BIRDS',1X,I5)
               ENDIF
               WRITE (11,5) MO,DA,YR,TIME,GRID1,GRID2,BIRDS
               GO TO 15
         32 CONTINUE
      *
         50 STOP
            END
      *------------------------------------------------------------*
```

5. Solution in text.

6.
```
      *------------------------------------------------------------*
            PROGRAM  CREATE2
      *
      * This program creates a direct access file from
      * a sequential file.
      *
```

221

```
       INTEGER  STOCK, QUANT, N
       CHARACTER  DESC*10, NAME*8
       REAL   PRICE
*
       PRINT*, 'ENTER THE NAME OF THE FILE TO BE CONVERTED: '
       READ*, NAME
       OPEN (UNIT=10,FILE=NAME,STATUS='OLD')
       OPEN (UNIT=11,FILE='EQUIP',ACCESS='DIRECT',
      +      STATUS='NEW',FORM='FORMATTED',RECL=23)
*
       N = 0
  10   READ (10,*,END=20) STOCK, DESC, QUANT, PRICE
          N = N + 1
          WRITE(11,15,REC=STOCK) STOCK, DESC, QUANT, PRICE
  15      FORMAT(I3,A,I4,F6.2)
          GO TO 10
  20   CONTINUE
*
       CLOSE(UNIT=11)
       OPEN (UNIT=11,FILE='EQUIP',ACCESS='DIRECT',
      +      STATUS='OLD',FORM='FORMATTED',RECL=23)
       DO 30 I = 1,N
          READ (11,15,REC=I,ERR=25) STOCK, DESC, QUANT, PRICE
          PRINT*, STOCK, DESC, QUANT, PRICE
  25      IF (I.NE.STOCK) PRINT*, 'NO RECORD NUMBER ', I
  30   CONTINUE
*
       END
*------------------------------------------------------------*
```

7. Solution in text.

8.
```
*------------------------------------------------------------*
       PROGRAM CHANGE
*
*  This program changes the description for selected stock
*  items in the inventory file.
*
       INTEGER  STOCK, CHANGE, QUANT, KEY
       LOGICAL  MORE
       CHARACTER*10  DESC
       REAL   PRICE
*
       DATA  MORE/.TRUE./
*
       OPEN (UNIT=10,FILE='EQUIP',ACCESS='DIRECT',
      +      STATUS='OLD',FORM='FORMATTED',RECL=23)
*
       PRINT*, 'ENTER STOCK NUMBER OF ITEM FOR WHICH DESCRIPTION'
       PRINT*, 'IS TO BE CHANGED (999 TO QUIT): '
       READ*, KEY
       IF (KEY.EQ.999) MORE = .FALSE.
*
  10   IF (MORE) THEN
          READ (10,15,REC=KEY,ERR=20,END=20)
```

```
      +                STOCK, DESC, QUANT, PRICE
   15       FORMAT(I3,A10,I4,F6.2)
            PRINT*, 'ENTER NEW DESCRIPTION: '
            READ*, DESC
            WRITE (10,15,REC=KEY) STOCK, DESC, QUANT, PRICE
   20       IF (KEY.NE.STOCK) THEN
                PRINT*, 'NO MATCH FOR ',KEY
                REWIND (UNIT=10)
            ENDIF
            PRINT*, 'ENTER STOCK NUMBER OF ITEM FOR WHICH DESCRIPTION'
            PRINT*, 'IS TO BE CHANGEDD (999 TO QUIT): '
            READ*, KEY
            IF (KEY.EQ.999) MORE = .FALSE.
            GO TO 10
        ENDIF
*
        END
*------------------------------------------------------------*


9.  *------------------------------------------------------------*
        PROGRAM  REORDER
*
*   This program prints a reorder report
*   for item with less than 5 units in the warehouse.
*
        INTEGER  KEY, STOCK, QUANT
        REAL  PRICE
        CHARACTER*10  DESC
*
        PRINT*, 'REORDER REPORT'
        PRINT*
        PRINT*, 'STOCK NUMBER     QUANTITY TO ORDER'
        OPEN (UNIT=11,FILE='EQUIP',ACCESS='DIRECT',
      +      STATUS='OLD',FORM='FORMATTED',RECL=23)
        KEY = 1
    5 READ (11,10,REC=KEY,ERR=20,END=20)
      +      STOCK,DESC,QUANT,PRICE
   10      FORMAT (I3,A10,I4,F6.2)
           IF (QUANT.LT.5) THEN
               PRINT 15, STOCK, 10 - QUANT
   15          FORMAT (1X,I3,20X,I2)
           ENDIF
           KEY = KEY + 1
           GO TO 5
*
   20 STOP
        END
*------------------------------------------------------------*


10. *------------------------------------------------------------*
        REAL FUNCTION TOTVAL( )
*
*   This function computes the total value
*   of all itlems in the warehouse.
*
```

223

```
          INTEGER  KEY, STOCK, QUANT
          REAL   PRICE
          CHARACTER*10  DESC
    *
          CLOSE (UNIT=11)
          OPEN (UNIT=11,FILE='EQUIP',ACCESS='DIRECT',
         +     STATUS='OLD',FORM='FORMATTED',RECL=23)
    *
          TOTVAL = 0.0
          KEY = 1
      10 READ (11,15,REC=KEY,ERR=20,END=20) STOCK, DESC,
         +                                  QUANT, PRICE
      15    FORMAT (I3,A10,I4,F6.2)
          TOTVAL = TOTVAL + PRICE*QUANT
          KEY = KEY + 1
          GO TO 10
      20 CLOSE UNIT=11)
    *
          RETURN
          END
    *------------------------------------------------------------*

11.  Solution in text.

12.  *------------------------------------------------------------*
          PROGRAM SALES
    *
    *  This program prints all the sales receipt numbers
    *  for a certain category number.
    *
          INTEGER  CATGRY, NUM, CODE, TEMP
    *
          OPEN(UNIT=10, FILE='SOFTWR', STATUS='OLD')
    *
          TEMP = 99999
    *
          PRINT*, 'ENTER THE CATEGORY NUMBER...'
          READ*, CATGRY
    *
          PRINT  10, CATGRY
      10 FORMAT(1X, 5X, 'SALES RECEIPT NUMBERS FOR',
         +          ' CATEGORY NUMBER ', I1)
          PRINT 15
      15 FORMAT(1X, 5X,
         +    '_____'/)
    *
      25 READ(10, 20, END=100) NUM, CODE
          IF ((CODE.EQ.CATGRY).AND.(TEMP.NE.NUM)) PRINT 30, NUM
          TEMP = NUM
          GO TO 25

      20 FORMAT(I5, 2X, I1)
      30 FORMAT(1X, 22X, I5)
    *
     100 STOP
```

224

```
                    ~

        END
*-----------------------------------------------------------*


13.  *-----------------------------------------------------------*
        INTEGER FUNCTION  COUNT(TYPE)
*
*    This function counts the number of
*    sales of a specified type of software.
*
        INTEGER  TYPE, NUM, CODE
*
        COUNT = 0
        OPEN (UNIT=10,FILE='SOFTWARE',STATUS='OLD')
      1 READ (10,5,END=20) NUM, CODE
      5    FORMAT (I5,2X,I1)
           IF (CODE.EQ.TYPE) COUNT = COUNT + 1
           GO TO 1
     20 CLOSE (UNIT=10)
*
        RETURN
        END
*-----------------------------------------------------------*


14.  *-----------------------------------------------------------*
        PROGRAM SALES
*
*    This program computes the monthly sales
*    information and prints a corresponding report.
*
        INTEGER  WORD, F77, PASCAL, C, GRAPHIC, CODE,
       +          NUM, TOTSAL, TOTPAC, TEMP
*
        DATA  WORD, F77, PASCAL, C, GRAPHIC, TOTSAL, TOTPAC
       +      /7*0/
*
        OPEN (UNIT=10, FILE='SOFTWR', STATUS='OLD')
*
        TEMP = 99999
*
      1 READ (10, 5, END=20) NUM, CODE
      5    FORMAT(I5, 2X, I1)
           IF (CODE.EQ.1) THEN
              WORD = WORD + 1
           ELSEIF (CODE.EQ.2) THEN
              F77 = F77 + 1
           ELSEIF (CODE.EQ.3) THEN
              PASCAL = PASCAL + 1
           ELSEIF (CODE.EQ.4) THEN
              C = C + 1
           ELSEIF (CODE.EQ.5) THEN
              GRAPHIC = GRAPHIC + 1
           ENDIF
           IF (TEMP.NE.NUM)   TOTSAL = TOTSAL + 1
           TOTPAC = TOTPAC + 1
           TEMP = NUM
```

225

```
          GO TO 1
*

   20 PRINT*, 'MONTHLY SOFTWARE SALES SUMMARY'
      PRINT*, 'CATEGROY              NUMBER OF SALES'
      PRINT*, '-----------------------------------'
      PRINT 25, WORD
   25 FORMAT(1X, 'WORDPROCESSER', 11X, I4)
      PRINT 30, F77
   30 FORMAT(1X, 'F77 COMPILER', 12X, I4)
      PRINT 35, PASCAL
   35 FORMAT(1X, 'PASCAL COMPILER', 9X, I4)
      PRINT 40, C
   40 FORMAT(1X, 'C COMPLIER', 14X, I4)
      PRINT 50, GRAPHIC
   50 FORMAT(1X, 'GRAPHICS PACKAGE', 8X, I4)
      PRINT 55, TOTSAL
   55 FORMAT(1X, 'TOTAL SALES RECEIPTS', 4X, I4)
      PRINT 60, TOTPAC
   60 FORMAT(1X, 'TOTAL PACKAGES', 10X, I4)
*

      END
*-----------------------------------------------------------*


15. *-----------------------------------------------------------*
      PROGRAM SALES
*
*  This program computes the monthly sales
*  information and prints a corresponding report.
*
      INTEGER  WORD, F77, PASCAL, C, GRAPHIC, CODE,
     +         NUM, CMPLRS, NUM1, NUM2, NUM3,
     +         COUNT, CURRNT
*
      DATA  WORD, F77, PASCAL, C, GRAPHIC, NUM1, NUM2, NUM3,
     +      CMPLRS, COUNT/10*0/
*
      OPEN (UNIT=10, FILE='SOFTWR', STATUS='OLD')
    1 READ (10, 5, END=10) NUM, CODE
    5    FORMAT(I5, 2X, I1)
         IF (CODE.EQ.1) THEN
            WORD = WORD + 1
         ELSEIF (CODE.EQ.2) THEN
            F77 = F77 + 1
            CMPLRS = CMPLRS + 1
         ELSEIF (CODE.EQ.3) THEN
            PASCAL = PASCAL + 1
            CMPLRS = CMPLRS + 1
         ELSEIF (CODE.EQ.4) THEN
            C = C + 1
            CMPLRS = CMPLRS + 1
         ELSEIF (CODE.EQ.5) THEN
            GRAPHIC = GRAPHIC + 1
         ENDIF
         GO TO 1
*
```

```
    10 REWIND(UNIT=10)
       READ(10, 5, END=20) NUM, CODE
       CURRNT = NUM
       IF ((CODE.EQ.2).OR.(CODE.EQ.3).OR.(CODE.EQ.4))
     +     COUNT = COUNT + 1
*
    15 READ(10, 5, END=20) NUM, CODE
          IF (CURRNT.EQ.NUM) THEN
             IF (CODE.EQ.2) THEN
                COUNT = COUNT + 1
             ELSEIF (CODE.EQ.3) THEN
                COUNT = COUNT + 1
             ELSEIF (CODE.EQ.4) THEN
                COUNT = COUNT + 1
             ENDIF
          ELSE
             IF (COUNT.EQ.1) THEN
                NUM1 = NUM1 + 1
             ELSEIF (COUNT.EQ.2) THEN
                NUM2 = NUM2 + 1
             ELSEIF (COUNT.EQ.3) THEN
                NUM3 = NUM3 + 1
             ENDIF
             BACKSPACE(UNIT=10)
             COUNT = 0
          ENDIF
          CURRNT = NUM
          GO TO 15
*
    20 PRINT*, 'MONTHLY SOFTWARE SALES SUMMARY'
       PRINT*, 'CATEGROY            NUMBER OF SALES'
       PRINT*, '-----------------------------------'
       PRINT 25, WORD
    25 FORMAT(1X, 'WORDPROCESSER', 11X, I4)
       PRINT 30, F77
    30 FORMAT(1X, 'F77 COMPILER', 12X, I4)
       PRINT 35, PASCAL
    35 FORMAT(1X, 'PASCAL COMPILER', 9X, I4)
       PRINT 40, C
    40 FORMAT(1X, 'C COMPLIER', 14X, I4)
       PRINT 50, GRAPHIC
    50 FORMAT(1X, 'GRAPHICS PACKAGE', 8X, I4)
       PRINT 55, CMPLRS
    55 FORMAT(1X, 'NUMBER OF COMPILERS SOLD', 17X, I4)
       PRINT 60, NUM1
    60 FORMAT(1X,'NUMBER OF RECEIPTS WITH ONE COMPILER',4X,I4)
       PRINT 65, NUM2
    65 FORMAT(1X,'NUMBER OF RECEIPTS WITH TWO COMPILERS',3X,I4)
       PRINT 70, NUM3
    70 FORMAT(1X,'NUMBER OF RECEIPTS WITH THREE COMPILERS',1X,I4)
*
       END
*-------------------------------------------------------------*

16. *-------------------------------------------------------------*
```

```
      PROGRAM SALES
*
*  This program computes the monthly sales
*  information and prints a corresponding report.
*
      INTEGER  WORD, F77, PASCAL, C, GRAPHIC, CODE,
     +         NUM, NUMWCP, CURRNT
*
      DATA  WORD, F77, PASCAL, C, GRAPHIC, NUM, NUMWCP
     +      /7*0/
*
      OPEN (UNIT=10, FILE='SOFTWR', STATUS='OLD')
    1 READ (10, 5, END=10) NUM, CODE
    5    FORMAT( I5, 2X, I1)
         IF (CODE.EQ.1) THEN
            WORD = WORD + 1
         ELSEIF (CODE.EQ.2) THEN
            F77 = F77 + 1
         ELSEIF (CODE.EQ.3) THEN
            PASCAL = PASCAL + 1
         ELSEIF (CODE.EQ.4) THEN
            C = C + 1
         ELSEIF (CODE.EQ.5) THEN
            GRAPHIC = GRAPHIC + 1
         ENDIF
      GO TO 1
*
   10 REWIND(UNIT=10)
   11 READ (10, 5, END=20) NUM, CODE
         IF (CODE.EQ.5) THEN
            CURRNT = NUM
            READ(10, 5, END=20) NUM, CODE
   13          IF (CURRNT.EQ.NUM) THEN
                  IF ((CODE.EQ.2).OR.(CODE.EQ.3).OR.
     +                (CODE.EQ.4)) NUMWCP = NUMWCP + 1
                  CURRNT = NUM
                  READ(10, 5, END=20) NUM, CODE
                  GO TO 13
               ENDIF
         ELSEIF (CODE.NE.1) THEN
            CURRNT = NUM
            READ (10, 5, END=20) NUM, CODE
   17       IF (CURRNT.EQ.NUM) THEN
               IF (CODE.EQ.5)  NUMWCP = NUMWCP + 1
               CURRNT = NUM
               READ(10, 5, END=20) NUM, CODE
               GO TO 17
            ENDIF
         ENDIF
         GO TO 11
*
   20 PRINT*, 'MONTHLY SOFTWARE SALES SUMMARY'
      PRINT*, 'CATEGROY             NUMBER OF SALES'
      PRINT*, '----------------------------------'
      PRINT 25, WORD
```

```
   25 FORMAT(1X, 'WORDPROCESSER', 11X, I4)
      PRINT 30, F77
   30 FORMAT(1X, 'F77 COMPILER', 12X, I4)
      PRINT 35, PASCAL
   35 FORMAT(1X, 'PASCAL COMPILER', 9X, I4)
      PRINT 40, C
   40 FORMAT(1X, 'C COMPLIER', 14X, I4)
      PRINT 50, GRAPHIC
   50 FORMAT(1X, 'GRAPHICS PACKAGE', 8X, I4)
      PRINT 55, WORD
   55 FORMAT(1X, 'NUMBER OF WORD PROCESSORS SOLD ', 20X, I4)
      PRINT 60, WORD-NUMWCP
   60 FORMAT(1X,'NUMBER OF WORD PROCESSORS SOLD SEPERATELY',
     +      10X, I4)
      PRINT 65, NUMWCP
   65 FORMAT(1X,'NUMBER OF WORD PROCESSORS SOLD WITH ',
     +      'A COMPILER',5X,I4)
   *
      END
   *------------------------------------------------------------*


17.   *------------------------------------------------------------*
      PROGRAM SALES
   *
   * This program prints all the sales receipt numbers
   * for sales of graphics packages.
   *
      INTEGER  I, J, NUM, CODE, RECPTS(4)
      LOGICAL  FULL
   *
      OPEN(UNIT=10, FILE='SOFTWR', STATUS='OLD')
   *
      I = 1
      FULL = .FALSE.
   *
      PRINT*, 'SALES RECEIPTS FOR GRAPHICS PACKAGES'
   *
   25 READ(10, 20, END=100) NUM, CODE
   20    FORMAT(I5, 2X, I1)
         IF (CODE.EQ.5) THEN
            RECPTS(I) = NUM
            IF (I.EQ.4)  FULL = .TRUE.
            IF (FULL) THEN
               PRINT 30, RECPTS(1), RECPTS(2), RECPTS(3), RECPTS(4)
   30          FORMAT(1X, 2X, I5, 4X, I5, 3X, I5, 3X, I5)
               I = 0
               DO 35 J = 1, 4
                  RECPTS(J) = 0
   35          CONTINUE
               FULL = .FALSE.
            ENDIF
            I = I + 1
         ENDIF
      GO TO 25
   *
```

229

```
      100 IF (.NOT.FULL) PRINT 30, RECPTS(1), RECPTS(2),
         +                          RECPTS(3), RECPTS(4)
      *
          END
      *-------------------------------------------------------------*
```

18.
```
      *-------------------------------------------------------------*
          PROGRAM CMPLIT
      *
      *   This program prints a list of employee numbers for
      *   employees that took the computer-literacy course.
      *
          INTEGER  NUMBER, I
          LOGICAL  DONE
          CHARACTER*30  NAME
          CHARACTER*4   TITLE, COURSE
      *
          OPEN (UNIT=10, FILE='TRAIN', STATUS='OLD')
      *
          TITLE = 'ECDM'
      *
          PRINT*, 'EMPLOYEES THAT TOOK COMPUTER LITERACY TEST'
          PRINT*, '               EMPLOYEE NUMBER               '
      *
       25 READ(10, 5, END= 30) NUMBER, NAME, COURSE
        5    FORMAT(I3, 1X, A30, 1X, A4)
      *
             I = 1
             DONE = .FALSE.
       10    IF (.NOT.DONE) THEN
                IF (COURSE(I:I).EQ.TITLE(2:2)) THEN
                   PRINT 15, NUMBER
       15          FORMAT(1X, 20X, I3)
                   DONE = .TRUE.
                ENDIF
                I = I + 1
                IF (I.GT.4)  DONE = .TRUE.
                GO TO 10
             ENDIF
      *
             GO TO 25
      *
       30 STOP
          END
      *-------------------------------------------------------------*
```

19.
```
      *-------------------------------------------------------------*
          PROGRAM COURSE
      *
      *   This program prints a list of employee numbers for employees
      *   that took each course:  electronics, computer literacy,
      *   digital logic design, and microprocessors.
      *
          INTEGER  NUMBER, I, J
          LOGICAL  DONE, FOUND
```

230

```
      CHARACTER*30  NAME
      CHARACTER*4   TITLE, COURSE
*
      TITLE = 'ECDM'
*
      OPEN (UNIT=10, FILE='TRAIN', STATUS='OLD')
*
      I = 1
      DONE = .FALSE.
*
      PRINT*, 'EMPLOYEES THAT HAVE TAKEN EACH COURSE, (BY NUMBER)'
      PRINT*, 'COURSE ORDER:  E, C, D, M'
*
    5 IF (.NOT.DONE) THEN
*
   10    READ(10, 15, END=35) NUMBER, NAME, COURSE
   15       FORMAT(I3, 1X, A30, 1X, A4)
*
           J = 1
           FOUND = .FALSE.
   20      IF (.NOT.FOUND) THEN
              IF (COURSE(J:J).EQ.TITLE(I:I)) THEN
                 PRINT 25, TITLE(I:I), NUMBER
   25            FORMAT(1X, 15X, A, 10X, I3)
                 FOUND = .TRUE.
              ENDIF
              J = J + 1
              IF (J.GT.4)  FOUND = .TRUE.
              GO TO 20
           ENDIF
           GO TO 5
   35      I = I + 1
           REWIND(UNIT=10)
           IF (I.GT.4)  DONE = .TRUE.
           GO TO 5
      ENDIF
*
      END
*-----------------------------------------------------------*

20. *-----------------------------------------------------------*
      PROGRAM PERCNT
*
* This program prints a summary report to give the
* percentage of students in each course:  electronics,
* computer literacy, digital logic design, and
* microprocessors.
      INTEGER  NUMBER, ELECT, CMPLIT, DIGLOG, MICRO,
     +         TOTAL, I, J
      CHARACTER*30  NAME
      CHARACTER*4  COURSE, TITLE
*
      DATA  ELECT, CMPLIT, DIGLOG, MICRO, TOTAL /5*0/
*
      TITLE = 'ECDM'
```

231

```
*
      OPEN(UNIT=10, FILE='TRAIN', STATUS='OLD')
*
    1 READ(10, 5, END=50) NUMBER, NAME, COURSE
    5    FORMAT (I3, 1X, A30, 1X, A4)
         TOTAL = TOTAL + 1
         DO 20 I = 1, 4
            J = 1
   10       IF (J.LE.4) THEN
               IF (COURSE(J:J).EQ.TITLE(I:I)) THEN
                  IF (I.EQ.1) THEN
                     ELECT = ELECT + 1
                  ELSEIF (I.EQ.2) THEN
                     CMPLIT = CMPLIT + 1
                  ELSEIF (I.EQ.3) THEN
                     DIGLOG = DIGLOG + 1
                  ELSEIF (I.EQ.4) THEN
                     MICRO = MICRO + 1
                  ENDIF
               ENDIF
               J = J + 1
               GO TO 10
            ENDIF
   20    CONTINUE
         GO TO 1
*
   50 PRINT*, 'SUMMARY OF TRAINING PROGRAM COURSES'
      PRINT*, 'COURSE                PERCENTAGE'
      PRINT*, '---------------------------------'
      PRINT 55, REAL(ELECT)/REAL(TOTAL)*100.0
   55 FORMAT(1X, 'ELECTRONICS', 11X, F5.1)
      PRINT 60, REAL(CMPLIT)/REAL(TOTAL)*100.0
   60 FORMAT(1X, 'COMPUTER LITERACY', 5X, F5.1)
      PRINT 65, REAL(DIGLOG)/REAL(TOTAL)*100.0
   65 FORMAT(1X, 'DIGITAL LOGIC DESIGN', 2X, F5.1)
      PRINT 70, REAL(MICRO)/REAL(TOTAL)*100.0
   70 FORMAT(1X, 'MICROPROCESSORS', 7X, F5.1)
*
      END
*-------------------------------------------------------------*

21. *-------------------------------------------------------------*
      PROGRAM ENROLLD
*
* This program prints the total enrollment in the courses
* electronics, computer literacy, digital logic design,
* microprocessors and the number of students in each.
*
      INTEGER  NUMBER, ELECT, CMPLIT, DIGLOG, MICRO,
     +         TOTAL, I, J
      CHARACTER*30  NAME
      CHARACTER*4  COURSE, TITLE
*
      DATA  ELECT, CMPLIT, DIGLOG, MICRO, TOTAL /5*0/
*
```

```
           TITLE = 'ECDM'
*
           OPEN(UNIT=10, FILE='TRAIN', STATUS='OLD')
*
        1 READ(10, 5, END=50) NUMBER, NAME, COURSE
        5    FORMAT (I3, 1X, A30, 1X, A4)
*
           TOTAL = TOTAL + 1
*
           DO 20 I = 1, 4
              J = 1
       10     IF (J.LE.4) THEN
                 IF (COURSE(J:J).EQ.TITLE(I:I)) THEN
                    IF (I.EQ.1) THEN
                       ELECT = ELECT + 1
                    ELSEIF (I.EQ.2) THEN
                       CMPLIT = CMPLIT + 1
                    ELSEIF (I.EQ.3) THEN
                       DIGLOG = DIGLOG + 1
                    ELSEIF (I.EQ.4) THEN
                       MICRO = MICRO + 1
                    ENDIF
                 ENDIF
                 J = J + 1
                 GO TO 10
              ENDIF
       20     CONTINUE
           GO TO 1
*
       50 PRINT*, 'SUMMARY OF TRAINING PROGRAM COURSES'
          PRINT*, 'COURSE                  PERCENTAGE',
         +        '      TOTAL ENROLLMENT'
          PRINT*, '-------------------------------',
         +        '--------------------'
          PRINT 55, REAL(ELECT)/REAL(TOTAL)*100.0, ELECT
       55 FORMAT(1X, 'ELECTRONICS', 11X, F5.1, 15X, I3)
          PRINT 60, REAL(CMPLIT)/REAL(TOTAL)*100.0, CMPLIT
       60 FORMAT(1X, 'COMPUTER LITERACY', 5X, F5.1, 15X, I3)
          PRINT 65, REAL(DIGLOG)/REAL(TOTAL)*100.0, DIGLOG
       65 FORMAT(1X, 'DIGITAL LOGIC DESIGN', 2X, F5.1, 15X, I3)
          PRINT 70, REAL(MICRO)/REAL(TOTAL)*100.0, MICRO
       70 FORMAT(1X, 'MICROPROCESSORS', 7X, F5.1, 15X, I3)
          PRINT 75, TOTAL
       75 FORMAT(1X,'NUMBER OF DIFFERENT STUDENTS INVOLVED',4X,I3)
*
          END
*------------------------------------------------------------*
```

22.
```
*------------------------------------------------------------*
      PROGRAM COUNTS
*
* This program prints the number of students who only
* took 1 course, 2 courses, 3 courses, or 4 courses.
*
      INTEGER  NUMBER, ELECT, CMPLIT, DIGLOG, MICRO,
```

```
      +            TOTAL, I, J, K, NUM1, NUM2, NUM3, NUM4, COUNT,
      +            BLANKS
       CHARACTER*30  NAME
       CHARACTER*4   COURSE, TITLE
*
       DATA  ELECT, CMPLIT, DIGLOG, MICRO, TOTAL,
      +       NUM1, NUM2, NUM3, NUM4 /9*0/
*
       TITLE = 'ECDM'
*
       OPEN(UNIT=10, FILE='TRAIN', STATUS='OLD')
*
     1 READ(10, 5, END=50) NUMBER, NAME, COURSE
     5    FORMAT (I3, 1X, A30, 1X, A4)
          TOTAL = TOTAL + 1
          DO 20 I = 1, 4
             J = 1
    10       IF (J.LE.4) THEN
                IF (COURSE(J:J).EQ.TITLE(I:I)) THEN
                   IF (I.EQ.1) THEN
                      ELECT = ELECT + 1
                   ELSEIF (I.EQ.2) THEN
                      CMPLIT = CMPLIT + 1
                   ELSEIF (I.EQ.3) THEN
                      DIGLOG = DIGLOG + 1
                   ELSEIF (I.EQ.4) THEN
                      MICRO = MICRO + 1
                   ENDIF
                ENDIF
                J = J + 1
                GO TO 10
             ENDIF
    20    CONTINUE
*
          BLANKS = 0
          COUNT = 0
*
          DO 25 K = 1, 4
             IF (COURSE(K:K).EQ.' ')  BLANKS = BLANKS + 1
    25    CONTINUE
*
          COUNT = 4 - BLANKS
          IF (COUNT.EQ.1) THEN
             NUM1 = NUM1 + 1
          ELSEIF (COUNT.EQ.2) THEN
             NUM2 = NUM2 + 1
          ELSEIF (COUNT.EQ.3) THEN
             NUM3 = NUM3 + 1
          ELSEIF (COUNT.EQ.4) THEN
             NUM4 = NUM4 + 1
          ENDIF
          GO TO 1
*
    50 PRINT*, 'SUMMARY OF TRAINING PROGRAM COURSES'
       PRINT*, 'COURSE                 PERCENTAGE'
```

```
      PRINT*, '------------------------------------'
      PRINT 55, REAL(ELECT)/REAL(TOTAL)*100.0
   55 FORMAT(1X, 'ELECTRONICS', 11X, F5.1)
      PRINT 60, REAL(CMPLIT)/REAL(TOTAL)*100.0
   60 FORMAT(1X, 'COMPUTER LITERACY', 5X, F5.1)
      PRINT 65, REAL(DIGLOG)/REAL(TOTAL)*100.0
   65 FORMAT(1X, 'DIGITAL LOGIC DESIGN', 2X, F5.1)
      PRINT 70, REAL(MICRO)/REAL(TOTAL)*100.0
   70 FORMAT(1X, 'MICROPROCESSORS', 7X, F5.1)
      PRINT 75, NUM1
   75 FORMAT(1X, 'NUMBER OF STUDENTS WHO TOOK 1 COURSE ', I3)
      PRINT 80, NUM2
   80 FORMAT(1X, 'NUMBER OF STUDENTS WHO TOOK 2 COURSES', I3)
      PRINT 85, NUM3
   85 FORMAT(1X, 'NUMBER OF STUDENTS WHO TOOK 3 COURSES', I3)
      PRINT 90, NUM4
   90 FORMAT(1X, 'NUMBER OF STUDENTS WHO TOOK 4 COURSES', I3)
*
      END
*-------------------------------------------------------------*
```

Chapter 10

1.   Solution in text.

2.   *--*
```
         PROGRAM  LINEAR
*
*    This program computes a linear model for XY data and
*    then computes the resudual sum to evaluate the model
*
         INTEGER  I, N
         REAL   X(500),Y(500),SLOPE,YINT,YNEW,RES,
        +       SUMX,SUMY,SUMXY,SUMXX,SUMRES
*
         DATA   I,SUMX,SUMY,SUMXY, SUMXX, SUMRES /1,5*0/
*
         OPEN (UNIT=10,FILE='XYDATA',STATUS='OLD')
       5 READ (10,*,END=50) X(I), Y(I)
            SUMX = SUMX + X(I)
            SUMY = SUMY + Y(I)
            SUMXY = SUMXY + X(I)*Y(I)
            SUMXX = SUMXX + X(I)*X(I)
            I = I + 1
            GO TO 5
*
      50 N = I - 1
         SLOPE = (SUMX*SUMY - REAL(N)*SUMXY)/
        +        (SUMX*SUMX - REAL(N)*SUMXX)
         YINT = (SUMY - SLOPE*SUMX)/REAL(N)
*
         PRINT*, 'THE LINEAR EQUATION IS'
         PRINT 55, SLOPE, YINT
      55 FORMAT (1X,'Y = ',F6.2,' X + ',F6.2)
         PRINT*
         PRINT*, 'ORIGINAL   ORIGINAL    ESTIMATED    RESIDUAL'
         PRINT*, '   X          Y           Y                '
         PRINT*
*
         DO 65 I=1,N
            YNEW = SLOPE*X(I) + YINT
            RES = ABS(Y(I) - YNEW)
            SUMRES = SUMRES + RES
            PRINT 60, X(I), Y(I), YNEW, RES
      60    FORMAT (1X,F6.2,6X,F6.2,6X,F6.2,7X,F6.2)
      65 CONTINUE
*
         PRINT*
         PRINT 70, SUMRES
      70 FORMAT (1X, 'RESIDUAL SUM = ', F6.2)
*
         END
```
     --

3.   *--*
```
         PROGRAM  LINEAR
```

```
*
*   This program computes a linear model for XY data and
*   then computes the resudual sum to evaluate the model.
*
      INTEGER  I, N
      REAL  X(500), Y(500), SLOPE, YINT, YNEW, RES, SUMRES
*
      OPEN (UNIT=10,FILE='XYDATA',STATUS='OLD')
      I = 1
      SUMRES = 0.0
    5 READ (10,*,END=50) X(I), Y(I)
         I = I + 1
         GO TO 5
   50 N = I - 1
      CALL LINE(X,Y,N,SLOPE,YINT)
      PRINT*, 'THE LINEAR EQUATION IS'
      PRINT 55, SLOPE, YINT
   55 FORMAT (1X,'Y = ',F6.2,' X + ',F6.2)
      PRINT*
      PRINT*, 'ORIGINAL   ORIGINAL     ESTIMATED     RESIDUAL'
      PRINT*, '   X          Y            Y                  '
      PRINT*
*
      DO 65 I=1,N
         YNEW = SLOPE*X(I) + YINT
         RES = Y(I) - YNEW
         SUMRES = SUMRES + RES*RES
         PRINT 60, X(I), Y(I), YNEW, RES
   60    FORMAT (1X,F6.2,6X,F6.2,6X,F6.2,7X,F6.2)
   65 CONTINUE
*
      PRINT*
      PRINT 70, SUMRES
   70 FORMAT (1X,'RESIDUAL SUM = ',F6.2)
*
      END
*---------------------------------------------------------------*
      SUBROUTINE  LINE(X,Y,N,SLOPE,YINT)
*
*   This subroutine computes the slope and
*   y intercepts for a linear model.
*
      INTEGER  N, I
      REAL  X(N), Y(N), SLOPE, YINT,
     +      SUMX, SUMY, SUMXY, SUMXX
*
      SUMX = 0.0
      SUMY = 0.0
      SUMXY = 0.0
      SUMXX = 0.0
      DO 10 I=1,N
         SUMX = SUMX + X(I)
         SUMY = SUMY + Y(I)
         SUMXY = SUMXY + X(I)*Y(I)
         SUMXX = SUMXX + X(I)*X(I)
```

237

```
    10 CONTINUE
       SLOPE = (SUMX*SUMY - REAL(N)*SUMXY)/
      +         (SUMX*SUMX - REAL(N)*SUMXX)
       YINT = (SUMY - SLOPE*SUMX)/REAL(N)
*
       RETURN
       END
*------------------------------------------------------------*

4.     *------------------------------------------------------------*
       PROGRAM  LINEAR
*
*  This program computes a linear model for XY data and
*  then computes the resudual sum to evaluate the model
*
       INTEGER  I, N
       REAL   X(500),Y(500),SLOPE,YINT,YNEW,RES,
      +       SUMX,SUMY,SUMXY,SUMXX,SUMRES
*
       DATA   I,SUMX,SUMY,SUMXY, SUMXX, SUMRES /1,5*0/
*
       OPEN (UNIT=10,FILE='XYDATA',STATUS='OLD')
       READ (10,*,END=50) X(I), Y(I)
     5 IF  (X(I).NE.-999.AND.Y(I).NE.-999) THEN
          SUMX = SUMX + X(I)
          SUMY = SUMY + Y(I)
          SUMXY = SUMXY + X(I)*Y(I)
          SUMXX = SUMXX + X(I)*X(I)
          I = I + 1
          READ (10,*,END=50) X(I), Y(I)
          GO TO 5
       ENDIF
*
    50 N = I - 1
       SLOPE = (SUMX*SUMY - REAL(N)*SUMXY)/
      +         (SUMX*SUMX - REAL(N)*SUMXX)
       YINT = (SUMY - SLOPE*SUMX)/REAL(N)
*
       PRINT*, 'THE LINEAR EQUATION IS'
       PRINT 55, SLOPE, YINT
    55 FORMAT (1X,'Y = ',F6.2,' X + ',F6.2)
       PRINT*
       PRINT*, 'ORIGINAL   ORIGINAL     ESTIMATED    RESIDUAL'
       PRINT*, '   X          Y            Y                 '
       PRINT*
*
       DO 65 I=1,N
          YNEW = SLOPE*X(I) + YINT
          RES = Y(I) - YNEW
          SUMRES = SUMRES + RES*RES
          PRINT 60, X(I), Y(I), YNEW, RES
    60    FORMAT (1X,F6.2,6X,F6.2,6X,F6.2,7X,F6.2)
    65 CONTINUE
*
       PRINT*
```

```
          PRINT 70, SUMRES
       70 FORMAT (1X, 'RESIDUAL SUM = ', F6.2)
*

          END
*------------------------------------------------------------*


5.    *------------------------------------------------------------*
          PROGRAM  LINEAR
*
*  This program computes a linear model for XY data and
*  then computes the resudual sum to evaluate the model.
*
          INTEGER  I, N
          REAL   X(500),Y(500),SLOPE,YINT,YNEW,RES,
        +        SUMX,SUMY,SUMXY,SUMXX,SUMRES,XNEW,YNEW
*
          DATA   I,SUMX,SUMY,SUMXY, SUMXX, SUMRES /1,5*0.0/
*
          OPEN (UNIT=10,FILE='XYDATA',STATUS='OLD')
*
        5 READ (10,*,END=50) X(I), Y(I)
              SUMX  = SUMX + X(I)
              SUMY  = SUMY + Y(I)
              SUMXY = SUMXY + X(I)*Y(I)
              SUMXX = SUMXX + X(I)*X(I)
              I = I + 1
              GO TO 5
*
       50 N = I - 1
          SLOPE = (SUMX*SUMY - REAL(N)*SUMXY)/
        +         (SUMX*SUMX - REAL(N)*SUMXX)
          YINT = (SUMY - SLOPE*SUMX)/REAL(N)
*
          PRINT*, 'THE LINEAR EQUATION IS'
          PRINT 55, SLOPE, YINT
       55 FORMAT (1X,'Y = ',F6.2,' X + ',F6.2)
          PRINT*
          PRINT*, 'ORIGINAL   ORIGINAL    ESTIMATED    RESIDUAL'
          PRINT*, '   X          Y            Y                '
          PRINT*
*
          DO 65 I=1,N
              YNEW = SLOPE*X(I) + YINT
              RES = Y(I) - YNEW
              SUMRES = SUMRES + RES*RES
              PRINT 60, X(I), Y(I), YNEW, RES
       60     FORMAT (1X,F6.2,6X,F6.2,6X,F6.2,7X,F6.2)
       65 CONTINUE
*
          PRINT*
          PRINT 70, SUMRES
       70 FORMAT (1X, 'RESIDUAL SUM = ', F6.2)
          PRINT*
          PRINT*, 'ENTER X COORDINATE'
          READ*, XNEW
```

```
              YNEW = SLOPE*XNEW + YINT
              PRINT 75, YNEW
         75 FORMAT (1X,'CORRESPONDING Y COORDINATE IS ',F6.2)
      *
              END
      *----------------------------------------------------------------*

6.    *----------------------------------------------------------------*
              PROGRAM  AREA1
      *
      *  This program estimates the area under a given curve.
      *
              INTEGER  N, I
              REAL  A, B, BASE, LEFT, RIGHT, AREA, SUM
      *
              F(X) = 4.0*EXP(-(X - 2.0)**2)
      *
              PRINT*, 'ENTER THE INTERVAL ENDPOINTS: '
              READ*, A, B
              PRINT*, 'ENTER THE NUMBER OF TRAPEZOIDS (0 TO QUIT): '
              READ*, N
      *
          5 IF (N.NE.0) THEN
              SUM = 0.0
              BASE = (B - A)/REAL(N)
              LEFT = F(A)
              RIGHT = F(A + BASE)
      *
              DO 10 I=1,N
                  AREA = 0.5*BASE*(LEFT + RIGHT)
                  SUM = SUM + AREA
                  LEFT = RIGHT
                  RIGHT = F(BASE*(I + 1) + A)
         10     CONTINUE
      *
              PRINT 15, N, SUM
         15     FORMAT (1X,'USING ',I3,' TRAPEZOIDS, ',
              +            'THE ESTIMATED AREA IS ',F7.3)
      *
              PRINT*, 'ENTER THE NUMBER OF TRAPEZOIDS (0 TO QUIT): '
              READ*, N
              GO TO 5
            ENDIF
      *
            END
      *----------------------------------------------------------------*

7.    Solution in text.

8.    *----------------------------------------------------------------*
              PROGRAM  AREA1
      *
      *  This program estimates the area under a given curve.
      *
              INTEGER  N, I
```

240

```
      REAL  A, B, BASE, LEFT, RIGHT, AREA, SUM, OLD, TOL
      LOGICAL  DONE
*
      F(X) = 4.0*EXP(-(X - 2.0)**2)
*
      DATA  SUM, DONE  /0.0, .FALSE./
*
      PRINT*, 'ENTER THE INTERVAL ENDPOINTS: '
      READ*, A, B
      PRINT*, 'ENTER THE TOLERANCE VALUE: '
      READ*, TOL
      N = 10
*
    5 IF (.NOT.DONE) THEN
         BASE = (B - A)/REAL(N)
         LEFT = F(A)
         RIGHT = F(A + BASE)
*
         DO 10 I=1,N
            AREA = 0.5*BASE*(LEFT + RIGHT)
            SUM = SUM + AREA
            LEFT = RIGHT
            RIGHT = F(BASE*(I + 1) + A)
   10    CONTINUE
         IF (N.EQ.10) THEN
            OLD = SUM
            N = N*2
            SUM = 0.0
         ELSE
            IF (ABS(SUM - OLD).LT.TOL) THEN
               DONE = .TRUE.
            ELSE
               OLD = SUM
               N = N*2
               SUM = 0.0
            ENDIF
         ENDIF
         GO TO 5
      ENDIF
*
      PRINT 15, N, SUM
   15 FORMAT (1X,'USING ',I3,' TRAPEZOIDS, ',
     +        'THE ESTIMATED AREA IS ',F7.3)
*
      END
*----------------------------------------------------------*


9.  *----------------------------------------------------------*
      PROGRAM  AREA1
*
*  This program estimates the area under a given curve.
*
      INTEGER  N, I
      REAL  A, B, BASE, LEFT, RIGHT, AREA, SUM, F
*
```

```
      DATA  SUM /0.0/
*
      PRINT*, 'ENTER THE INTERVAL ENDPOINTS: '
      READ*, A, B
      PRINT*, 'ENTER THE NUMBER OF TRAPEZOIDS: '
      READ*, N
*
      BASE = (B - A)/REAL(N)
      LEFT = F(A)
      RIGHT = F(A + BASE)
*
      DO 10 I=1,N
         AREA = 0.5*BASE*(LEFT + RIGHT)
         SUM = SUM + AREA
         LEFT = RIGHT
         RIGHT = F(BASE*(I + 1) + A)
   10 CONTINUE
*
      PRINT 15, N, SUM
   15 FORMAT (1X,'USING ',I3,' TRAPEZOIDS, ',
     +         'THE ESTIMATED AREA IS ',F7.3)
*
      END
*------------------------------------------------------------------*
      REAL FUNCTION  F(X)
*
*  This function computes a value for
*  an exponential function.
*
      REAL  X
*
      F = 4.0*EXP(-(X - 2.0)**2)
*
      RETURN
      END
*----------------------------------------------------------------*
```

10.
```
*----------------------------------------------------------------*
      PROGRAM  AREA1
*
*  This program estimates the area under a given curve.
*
      INTEGER  N, I
      REAL  A, B, BASE, LEFT, RIGHT, AREA, SUM
*
      F(X) = 4.0*EXP(-(X - 2.0)**2)
*
      DATA  SUM /0.0/
      OPEN (UNIT=10,FILE='SAVEPT',STATUS='NEW')
*
      PRINT*, 'ENTER THE INTERVAL ENDPOINTS: '
      READ*, A, B
      PRINT*, 'ENTER THE NUMBER OF TRAPEZOIDS: '
      READ*, N
*
```

```
      BASE = (B - A)/REAL(N)
      LEFT = F(A)
      RIGHT = F(A + BASE)
      WRITE (10,*) A, LEFT
*
      DO 10 I=1,N
         AREA = 0.5*BASE*(LEFT + RIGHT)
         SUM = SUM + AREA
         LEFT = RIGHT
         RIGHT = F(BASE*(I + 1) + A)
         WRITE (10,*) BASE*(I + 1) + A, RIGHT
   10 CONTINUE
*
      PRINT 15, N, SUM
   15 FORMAT (1X,'USING ',I3,' TRAPEZOIDS, ',
     +        'THE ESTIMATED AREA IS ',F7.3)
*
      END
*------------------------------------------------------------*
```

11. Solution in text.

12.
```
*------------------------------------------------------------*
      PROGRAM  POLY
*
* This program determines the roots in an interval
* for a quartic polynomial using interval halving.
*
      INTEGER  COUNT
      REAL  LEFT, RIGHT, P, INT
*
      COMMON  /COEFF/ A, B, C, D, E
*
      PRINT*, 'ENTER COEFFICIENTS A, B, C, D, E'
      READ*, A, B, C, D, E
      PRINT*, 'ENTER THE INTERVAL SIZE: '
      READ*, INT
    1 IF (A.NE.0.0.OR.B.NE.0.0.OR.C.NE.0.0.OR.
     +    D.NE.0.0.OR.E.NE.0.0) THEN
*
         PRINT*
         PRINT*, 'POLYNOMIAL:'
         PRINT 5
    5    FORMAT (1X,'           4              3',
     +           '                2')
         PRINT 10, A, B, C, D, E
   10    FORMAT (1X,4(F7.3,' X  + '),F7.3)
         PRINT*
*
         COUNT = 0
         LEFT = -5.0
         RIGHT = LEFT + INT
         N = NINT((5.0 - (-5.0))/INT)
         DO 20 I=1,N
            IF (P(LEFT).EQ.0.0) THEN
```

243

```
                  PRINT 15, LEFT, P(LEFT)
      15          FORMAT (1X,'ROOT = ',F7.3,
       +                   '    P(ROOT) = ',F7.3)
                  COUNT = COUNT + 1
              ELSEIF (P(LEFT)*P(RIGHT).LT.0.0) THEN
                  CALL ITERAT (LEFT,RIGHT,ROOT)
                  PRINT 15, ROOT, P(ROOT)
                  COUNT = COUNT + 1
              ENDIF
              LEFT = RIGHT
              RIGHT = LEFT + INT
      20    CONTINUE
          IF (P(LEFT).EQ.0.0) THEN
              PRINT 15, LEFT, P(LEFT)
              COUNT = COUNT + 1
          ENDIF
          IF (COUNT.EQ.0) THEN
              PRINT*, 'NO ROOTS IN INTERVAL [-5,5]'
          ENDIF
          PRINT*
          PRINT*, 'ENTER COEFFICIENTS A, B, C, D, E'
          PRINT*, '(ALL ZEROS TO QUIT) '
          READ*, A, B, C, D, E
          GO TO 1
      ENDIF
*
      END
*----------------------------------------------------------*

13.  *----------------------------------------------------------*
      PROGRAM  POLY
*
*  This program determines  the roots in the interval [-5,5]
*  for a quartic polynomial using interval halving.
*
      INTEGER  COUNT
      REAL  LEFT, RIGHT, P, MAX, MIN
*
      COMMON  /COEFF/ A, B, C, D, E
*
      PRINT*, 'ENTER COEFFICIENTS A, B, C, D, E'
      READ*, A, B, C, D, E
    1 IF (A.NE.0.0.OR.B.NE.0.0.OR.C.NE.0.0.OR.
      +    D.NE.0.0.OR.E.NE.0.0) THEN
*
          PRINT*
          PRINT*, 'POLYNOMIAL:'
          PRINT 5
      5    FORMAT (1X,'          4              3',
       +             '              2')
          PRINT 10, A, B, C, D, E
      10   FORMAT (1X,4(F7.3,' X  + '),F7.3)
          PRINT*
*
          COUNT = 0
```

244

```
          LEFT = -5.0
          RIGHT = -4.75
          MAX = P(LEFT)
          MIN = P(LEFT)
          DO 20 I=1,40
             IF (P(LEFT).EQ.0.0) THEN
                PRINT 15, LEFT, P(LEFT)
15              FORMAT (1X,'ROOT = ',F7.3,
     +                   '    P(ROOT) = ',F7.3)
                COUNT = COUNT + 1
             ELSEIF (P(LEFT)*P(RIGHT).LT.0.0) THEN
                CALL ITERAT (LEFT,RIGHT,ROOT)
                PRINT 15, ROOT, P(ROOT)
                COUNT = COUNT + 1
             ENDIF
             IF (P(RIGHT).GT.MAX) MAX = P(RIGHT)
             IF (P(RIGHT).LT.MIN) MIN = P(RIGHT)
             LEFT = RIGHT
             RIGHT = LEFT + 0.25
20        CONTINUE
             IF (P(LEFT).EQ.0.0) THEN
                PRINT 15, LEFT, P(LEFT)
                COUNT = COUNT + 1
             ENDIF
          IF (COUNT.EQ.0) THEN
              PRINT*, 'NO ROOTS IN INTERVAL [-5,5]'
          ENDIF
          PRINT 25, MAX, MIN
25        FORMAT (1X,'MAXIMUM VALUE = ',F8.2,
     +              '; MINIMUM VALUE = ',F8.2)
          PRINT*
          PRINT*, 'ENTER COEFFICIENTS A, B, C, D, E'
          PRINT*, '(ALL ZEROS TO QUIT)'
          READ*, A, B, C, D, E
          GO TO 1
       ENDIF
*
       END
*-------------------------------------------------------*
       (no changes in function P)
*-------------------------------------------------------*
       (no changes in subroutine ITERAT)
*-------------------------------------------------------*

14.  *-------------------------------------------------------*
       PROGRAM  POLY
*
* This program determines the roots in an interval
* for a quartic polynomial using interval halving.
*
       INTEGER  COUNT, ITS
       REAL  LEFT, RIGHT, P
*
       COMMON  /COEFF/ A, B, C, D, E
*
```

```fortran
      PRINT*, 'ENTER COEFFICIENTS A, B, C, D, E'
      READ*, A, B, C, D, E
    1 IF (A.NE.0.0.OR.B.NE.0.0.OR.C.NE.0.0.OR.
     +    D.NE.0.0.OR.E.NE.0.0) THEN
*
         PRINT*
         PRINT*, 'POLYNOMIAL:'
         PRINT 5
    5    FORMAT (1X,'           4              3',
     +                ',                 2')
         PRINT 10, A, B, C, D, E
   10    FORMAT (1X,4(F7.3,' X  + '),F7.3)
         PRINT*
*
         COUNT = 0
         LEFT = -5.0
         RIGHT = -4.75
         DO 20 I=1,40
            IF (P(LEFT).EQ.0.0) THEN
               PRINT 15, LEFT, P(LEFT)
   15          FORMAT (1X,'ROOT = ',F7.3,
     +                    '    P(ROOT) = ',F7.3)
               COUNT = COUNT + 1
            ELSEIF (P(LEFT)*P(RIGHT).LT.0.0) THEN
               CALL ITERAT (LEFT,RIGHT,ROOT,ITS)
               PRINT 15, ROOT, P(ROOT)
               COUNT = COUNT + 1
            ENDIF
            LEFT = RIGHT
            RIGHT = LEFT + 0.25
   20    CONTINUE
         IF (P(LEFT).EQ.0.0) THEN
            PRINT 15, LEFT, P(LEFT)
            COUNT = COUNT + 1
         ENDIF
         PRINT*
         IF (COUNT.EQ.0) THEN
            PRINT*, 'NO ROOTS IN INTERVAL [-5,5]'
         ELSE
            PRINT 25, ITS
   25       FORMAT (1X,I3,' ITERATIONS WERE REQUIRED',
     +                  ' TO FIND THE ROOTS')
         ENDIF
         PRINT*
         PRINT*, 'ENTER COEFFICIENTS A, B, C, D, E'
         PRINT*, '(ALL ZEROS TO QUIT) '
         READ*, A, B, C, D, E
         GO TO 1
      ENDIF
*
      END
*------------------------------------------------------------*
      (no changes in function P)
*------------------------------------------------------------*
*
```

```
      SUBROUTINE  ITERAT(LEFT,RIGHT,ROOT,ITS)
*
*  This subroutine uses interval halving to find a root.
*
      INTEGER  ITS
      REAL  LEFT,RIGHT,ROOT,SIZE,MID
      LOGICAL  DONE
*
      COMMON  /COEFF/ A,B,C,D,E
*
      ITS = 0
      DONE = .FALSE.
      SIZE = RIGHT - LEFT
    5 IF (SIZE.GT.0.01.AND..NOT.DONE) THEN
         MID = (LEFT + RIGHT)/2.0
         IF (P(MID).EQ.0.0) THEN
            DONE = .TRUE.
         ELSEIF (P(MID)*P(LEFT).LT.0.0) THEN
            RIGHT = MID
         ELSE
            LEFT = MID
         ENDIF
         SIZE = RIGHT - LEFT
         ITS = ITS + 1
         GO TO 5
      ENDIF
*
      IF (SIZE.GT.0.01) THEN
         ROOT = MID
      ELSE
         ROOT = (LEFT + RIGHT)/2.0
      ENDIF
*
      RETURN
      END
*------------------------------------------------------------*
```

15.

```
*------------------------------------------------------------*
      PROGRAM  POLY
*
*  This program determines  the roots in the interval [-5,5]
*  for a quartic polynomimal using interval halving.
*
      INTEGER  COUNT
      REAL  LEFT, RIGHT, P
*
      COMMON  /COEFF/ A, B, C, D, E
*
      PRINT*, 'ENTER COEFFICIENTS A, B, C, D, E: '
      READ*, A, B, C, D, E
    1 IF (A.NE.0.0.OR.B.NE.0.0.OR.C.NE.0.0.OR.
     +    D.NE.0.0.OR.E.NE.0.0) THEN
*
         PRINT*
         PRINT*, 'POLYNOMIAL:'
```

```
           PRINT 5
     5     FORMAT (1X,'              4                3',
     +                 '                  2')
           PRINT 10, A, B, C, D, E
    10     FORMAT (1X,4(F7.3,' X  + '),F7.3)
           PRINT*
*
           COUNT = 0
           LEFT = -5.0
           RIGHT = -4.75
           DO 20 I=1,40
              IF (P(LEFT).EQ.0.0) THEN
                 PRINT 15, LEFT, P(LEFT)
    15           FORMAT (1X,'ROOT = ',F7.3,
     +                    '       P(ROOT) = ',F7.3)
                 COUNT = COUNT + 1
              ELSEIF (P(LEFT)*P(RIGHT).LT.0.0) THEN
                 CALL ITERAT (LEFT,RIGHT,ROOT)
                 PRINT 15, ROOT, P(ROOT)
                 COUNT = COUNT + 1
              ENDIF
              LEFT = RIGHT
              RIGHT = LEFT + 0.25
    20     CONTINUE
              IF (P(LEFT).EQ.0.0) THEN
                 PRINT 15, LEFT, P(LEFT)
                 COUNT = COUNT + 1
              ENDIF
           IF (COUNT.EQ.0) THEN
               PRINT*, 'NO ROOTS IN INTERVAL [-5,5]'
           ENDIF
           PRINT*
           PRINT*, 'ENTER COEFFICIENTS A, B, C, D, E'
           PRINT*, '(ALL ZEROS TO QUIT) '
           READ*, A, B, C, D, E
           GO TO 1
        ENDIF
*
        END
*-------------------------------------------------------------------*
        (no changes in function P)
*-------------------------------------------------------------------*
*
        SUBROUTINE  ITERAT(LEFT,RIGHT,ROOT)
*
*  This subroutine uses interval halving to find a root.
*
        REAL  LEFT, RIGHT, ROOT, MID
        LOGICAL  DONE
*
        COMMON  /COEFF/ A, B, C, D, E
*
        DONE = .FALSE.
      5 IF (.NOT.DONE) THEN
           MID = (LEFT + RIGHT)/2.0
```

248

```
                      IF (ABS(P(MID)).LT.0.01)  THEN
                         DONE = .TRUE.
                      ELSEIF (P(MID)*P(LEFT).LT.0.0)  THEN
                         RIGHT = MID
                      ELSE
                         LEFT = MID
                      ENDIF
                      GO TO 5
                   ENDIF
       *
                   IF (SIZE.GT.0.01) THEN
                      ROOT = MID
                   ELSE
                      ROOT = (LEFT + RIGHT)/2.0
                   ENDIF
       *
                   RETURN
                   END
```
---

16. *--*
```
             PROGRAM  EQN3
       *
       *  This program computes the solution to three
       *  simultaneous equations using determinants.
       *
             REAL A(3), B(3), C(3), D(3), DENOM, DET
       *
             OPEN(UNIT=10,FILE='COEFF',STATUS='OLD')
       *
             DO 10 I = 1,3
                READ(10,*) A(I), B(I), C(I), D(I)
         10    CONTINUE
       *
             DENOM = DET(A,B,C)
             IF (DENOM.EQ.0.0) THEN
                PRINT*, 'NO UNIQUE SOLUTION EXISTS'
             ELSE
                X = DET(D,B,C)/DENOM
                Y = DET(A,D,C)/DENOM
                Z = DET(A,B,D)/DENOM
                PRINT 5, X
          5     FORMAT (1X,'SOLUTION: X = ',F7.2)
                PRINT 6, Y
          6     FORMAT (1X,'          Y = ',F7.2)
                PRINT 7, Z
          7     FORMAT (1X,'          Z = ',F7.2)
             ENDIF
       *
             END
```
--
             (no changes in function DET)
--

17. Solution in text.

18.

```
*----------------------------------------------------------------*
      PROGRAM  EQN3
*
*  This program computes the solution to three
*  simultaneous equations using determinants.
*
      REAL A(3), B(3), C(3), D(3), DENOM, DET
      LOGICAL  PARAL
*
      PRINT*, 'EACH EQUATION SHOULD BE IN THIS FORM:'
      PRINT*, 'A*X + B*Y + C*Z = D'
      PRINT*, 'ENTER A,B,C,D FOR EQUATION 1'
      READ*, A(1), B(1), C(1), D(1)
      PRINT*, 'ENTER A,B,C,D FOR EQUATION 2'
      READ*, A(2), B(2), C(2), D(2)
      PRINT*, 'ENTER A,B,C,D FOR EQUATION 3'
      READ*, A(3), B(3), C(3), D(3)
      PRINT*
*
      DENOM = DET(A,B,C)
      IF (DENOM.EQ.0.0) THEN
         PRINT*, 'NO UNIQUE SOLUTION EXISTS'
      ELSE
         X = DET(D,B,C)/DENOM
         Y = DET(A,D,C)/DENOM
         Z = DET(A,B,D)/DENOM
         PRINT 5, X
5        FORMAT (1X,'SOLUTION: X = ',F7.2)
         PRINT 6, Y
6        FORMAT (1X,'          Y = ',F7.2)
         PRINT 7, Z
7        FORMAT (1X,'          Z = ',F7.2)
      ENDIF
*
      PRINT*
      IF (PARAL(A,B,C,D,1,2)) THEN
         PRINT*, 'EQUATIONS 1 AND 2 ARE PARALLEL PLANES'
      ENDIF
      IF (PARAL(A,B,C,D,2,3)) THEN
         PRINT*, 'EQUATIONS 2 AND 3 ARE PARALLEL PLANES'
      ENDIF
      IF (PARAL(A,B,C,D,3,1)) THEN
         PRINT*, 'EQUATIONS 3 AND 1 ARE PARALLEL PLANES'
      ENDIF
*
      END
*----------------------------------------------------------------*
      (no changes in function DET)
*----------------------------------------------------------------*
      LOGICAL FUNCTION  PARAL(A,B,C,D,I,J)
*
*  This function determines whether equations
*  I and J are parallel or not.
*
```

```
          REAL   SCALE, A(3), B(3), C(3), D(3)
          INTEGER  I, J
     *
          PARAL = .TRUE.
          SCALE = A(I)/A(J)
          IF (B(J)*SCALE.NE.B(I)) PARAL = .FALSE.
          IF (C(J)*SCALE.NE.C(I)) PARAL = .FALSE.
          IF (D(J)*SCALE.NE.D(I)) PARAL = .FALSE.
     *
          RETURN
          END
     *------------------------------------------------------------*
```

19. Solution in text.

20.
```
     *------------------------------------------------------------*
          SUBROUTINE  NORM(A,AROW,ACOL,NA)
     *
     *  This subroutine normalizes an array
     *  values between 0 and 1.
     *
          REAL   A(AROW,ACOL), NA(AROW,ACOL), MININ, MAXIM
          INTEGER  AROW, ACOL, I, J
     *
          MAXIM = -9.9E30
          MININ = 9.9E30
          DO 10 I=1,AROW
             DO 5 J=1,ACOL
                MININ = MIN(MININ,A(I,J))
       5     CONTINUE
      10 CONTINUE
     *
          DO 20 I=1,AROW
             DO 15 J=1,ACOL
                NA(I,J) = A(I,J) - MININ
                MAXIM = MAX(MAXIM,NA(I,J))
      15     CONTINUE
      20 CONTINUE
     *
          DO 30 I=1,AROW
             DO 25 J=1,ACOL
                NA(I,J) = NA(I,J)/MAXIM
      25     CONTINUE
      30 CONTINUE
     *
          RETURN
          END
     *------------------------------------------------------------*
```

21.
```
     *------------------------------------------------------------*
          PROGRAM  PIE
     *
     *  This program uses numerical integration to calculate 'pi'.
     *
          REAL   SUB, YTWO, YONE, XTWO, XONE, AREA, PI
```

```
      INTEGER  I , INPUT
*
      DATA  XONE, AREA /2*0.0/
*
      PRINT*
      PRINT*,' INPUT NUMBER OF SUBSECTIONS'
      PRINT*
      READ*, INPUT
*
      DO 5 I=1,INPUT
         XTWO = REAL(I)/REAL(INPUT)
         YONE = SQRT(1.0 - (XONE + (XTWO - XONE))**2)
         YTWO = SQRT(1.0 - XONE**2)
         SUB = (YTWO + YONE)/2.0*(XTWO - XONE)
         AREA = AREA + SUB
         XONE = XTWO
    5 CONTINUE
*
      PI = AREA*4.0
      PRINT*
      PRINT*,' THE CALCULATED VALUE OF PI IS = ',PI
      PRINT*,' USING ',INPUT,' SUBSECTIONS'
*
      END
*------------------------------------------------------------*
```

22.
```
*------------------------------------------------------------*
      PROGRAM  PIE
*
*  This program uses numerical integration to calculate 'pi'.
*
      DOUBLE PRECISION  SUB, YTWO, YONE, XTWO, XONE, AREA, PI
      INTEGER  I, INPUT
*
      DATA  XONE, AREA /2*0.0D+00/
*
      PRINT*
      PRINT*,' INPUT NUMBER OF SUBSECTIONS'
      PRINT*
      READ*, INPUT
*
      DO 5 I=1,INPUT
         XTWO = REAL(I)/REAL(INPUT)
         YONE = DSQRT(1.0D+00 - (XONE + (XTWO - XONE))**2)
         YTWO = DSQRT(1.0D+00 - XONE**2)
         SUB = (YTWO + YONE)/2.0D+00*(XTWO - XONE)
         AREA = AREA + SUB
         XONE = XTWO
    5 CONTINUE
*
      PI = AREA*4.0D+00
      PRINT*
      PRINT*,' THE CALCULATED VALUE OF PI IS = ',PI
      PRINT*,' USING ',INPUT,' SUBSECTIONS'
*
```

```
          END
     *----------------------------------------------------------------*


23.  *----------------------------------------------------------------*
          PROGRAM  PIE
     *
     *  This program uses numerical integration to calculate 'pi'.
     *
          REAL  SUB, YTWO, YONE, XTWO, XONE, AREA, PI
          INTEGER  I, INPUT
     *
          DO 10 INPUT = 100,1000,100
             XONE = 0.0
             AREA = 0.0
             PI = 0.0
     *
             DO 5 I = 1,INPUT
                XTWO = REAL(I)/REAL(INPUT)
                YONE = SQRT(1.0 - (XONE + (XTWO - XONE))**2)
                YTWO = SQRT(1.0D+00 - XONE**2)
                SUB = (YTWO + YONE)/2.0*(XTWO - XONE)
                AREA = AREA + SUB
                XONE = XTWO
       5     CONTINUE
     *
             PI = AREA*4.0
             PRINT*
             PRINT*,' THE CALCULATED VALUE OF PI IS = ',PI
             PRINT*,' USING ',INPUT,' SUBSECTIONS'
      10 CONTINUE
     *
          END
     *----------------------------------------------------------------*


24.  *----------------------------------------------------------------*
          PROGRAM  DIFF
     *
     *  This program calculates the slope between consecutive points.
     *
          REAL  XONE, YONE, XTWO, YTWO, MIDX, SLOPE
     *
          PRINT*
          PRINT*,' INPUT FIRST COORDINATE'
          READ*, XONE, YONE
     *
          PRINT*
          PRINT*,' INPUT SECOND COORDINATE'
          READ*, XTWO, YTWO
     *
          PRINT*
          PRINT*,' X POSITION, SLOPE'
          PRINT*
     *
       5 IF (XTWO.NE.-9999.0) THEN
             MIDX = (XTWO + XONE)/2.0
```

253

```
                  SLOPE = (YTWO - YONE)/(XTWO - XONE)
                  PRINT*, MIDX, SLOPE
                  XONE = XTWO
                  YONE = YTWO
                  PRINT*
                  PRINT*,'INPUT NEXT COORDINATE (-9999.0 LEAVES PROGRAM)'
                  READ*, XTWO, YTWO
                  GO TO 5
            ENDIF
      *
            END
      *------------------------------------------------------------*


25.   *------------------------------------------------------------*
            PROGRAM  DIFF
      *
      * This program determines when the sign of the slope changes.
      *
            REAL  XONE, YONE, XTWO, YTWO, MIDX, SLOPE
            INTEGER  SIGN, SIGNH
      *
            SIGNH = 1
            PRINT*
            PRINT*,' INPUT FIRST COORDINATE'
            READ*, XONE, YONE
      *
            PRINT*
            PRINT*,' INPUT SECOND COORDINATE'
            READ*, XTWO, YTWO
      *
          5 IF (XTWO.NE.-9999.0) THEN
                  MIDX = (XTWO + XONE)/2.0
                  SLOPE = (YTWO - YONE)/(XTWO - XONE)
                  SIGN = INT(SLOPE/ABS(SLOPE))
                  IF (SIGN.NE.SIGNH) THEN
                     WRITE(6,10) MIDX
         10         FORMAT (/,1X,'POINT OF MAXIMUM OR MINIMUM IN CURVE OCCU
             +              ' NEAR X COORDINATE VALUE ',F6.2,/)
                     SIGNH = SIGN
                  ENDIF
                  XONE = XTWO
                  YONE = YTWO
                  PRINT*,' INPUT NEXT COORDINATE (-9999.0 LEAVES PROGRAM)'
                  READ*, XTWO, YTWO
                  GOTO 5
            ENDIF
      *
            END
      *------------------------------------------------------------*
```